LAND OF PLENTY

HOLT, RINEHART AND WINSTON   NEW YORK

WHEELER McMILLEN

LAND OF PLENTY

The American Farm Story

ILLUSTRATED WITH PHOTOGRAPHS

Contents

LAND OF PLENTY

CHAPTER 1 # Hunger and Serfdom

Food—this has been the basic universal necessity of man since first he walked upon the earth. From the beginning, he was hungry. In fact, the job of finding food enough to eat has been his foremost occupation in all times and in all places.

For many thousands of years people more often than not went hungry. Only within the last two centuries has a portion of the human race learned how to provide itself with an adequate supply of food. Even today, however, more than half of the world's population is underfed. Bodies are picked up every day, for instance, in the streets of Bombay and Calcutta, victims of starvation.

A unique fact about the United States of America is that only twice, and only for short periods and in different places—both in the earliest colonial days—have white men experienced starvation. In each of these two unhappy times, the cause was soon discovered and corrected.

American farmers have always been free men. That is why Americans have long been the best-fed people in history.

In contrast, the farmers of the Old World, until very recent centuries, were usually slaves or serfs. Even if they had developed productive agricultural methods, they had little reason to put heart or hope into the extra effort. They knew that the lords and

3

tax gatherers would get most of the benefit; under the feudal system, farmers were not permitted to move or to seek other kinds of work. One historian even recounts that "the right to beat one's peasantry occasionally ran with the land."

Tyranny and hunger have been intimate companions during much of man's experience on earth. The long reign of Louis XIV, called "le Grand Monarque" or the "Sun King," illustrates this dismal fact. He was King of France for seventy-two years—from 1643 to 1715—longer than any ruler on record. France was then considered the most powerful, as well as the most cultured and civilized, nation in the world. The authority of the King was absolute. He was admired as the ideal and perfect ruler, whose royal manners were unexcelled. In constant hope of gaining favors from him, the nobility of all France clustered around the court. The magnificent palace was crowded with princes and dukes, counts and bishops, aristocratic ladies and greedy hangers on.

For the court's frequent banquets, peacocks and pheasants were regular dishes. King Louis himself was no small eater, judging by the report of one of his followers who wrote: "I have often seen the king consume four full plates of different kinds of soup, a whole pheasant, a partridge, a large dish of salad, two great slices of ham, mutton served with gravy and garlic, a plate of sweet cakes and on top of that fruit and hardboiled eggs."

There is also an account of a banquet served at a time when starvation threatened thousands of French people and the army was on short rations as it faced its English enemies. The table was adorned by a model of a besieged city, with trenches of frozen cake, siege machines made of sugar, and fish ponds of jelly.

While the resplendent guests at such banquets regaled themselves, hundreds of hungry paupers gathered at the palace gates, waiting for the "tablecloth." The tables of the rich in those times were covered not with linen but with baked dough, and after the feast the "bread" was thrown to the beggars to eat.

Yet, the luxurious living of the King and the nobles had to be paid for by the peasants. The nobles and the clergy were not taxed in those days; the peasants paid all the bills. The government contracted with a group of forty men, who agreed to fill the royal treasury with so many millions of francs each year; if they collected more they could keep the money. The peasants were usually required to pay about half of their produce to the tax collectors; in some instances the demands rose to eighty per cent. If need be, the tax agents did not hesitate to seize farm animals, tools, even the peasants' seeds and furniture.

Meanwhile, the banquets continued at the great palace of Versailles, even though from 1705 to 1708 unfavorable weather brought famine to France. People were driven to eating bark from trees, and bodies were found along the roadsides, their mouths stuffed with weeds. A million persons—one out of every twenty from the whole French population—are said to have died; some estimates put the figure much higher.

In 1715, the old Sun King died, and his great grandson, Louis XV, became the tyrant—not so strong, but even more irresponsible. Before the century ended, six more periods of disastrous famine swept France, and carried the next king and his queen to the guillotine. The violent French Revolution of 1789 brought an end to the old monarchy.

The famines and hunger of the seventeenth and eighteenth centuries were no new experience to France. Accounts tell of terrible famines as far back as the tenth and eleventh centuries. English records are little different. From 1200 to 1600, an average of ten years of famine was reported every hundred years. Also in Germany, Poland, Russia, India, China, Turkey—wherever populations grew—starvation helped to limit the numbers. Hunger weakens bodies and makes all ages susceptible to diseases.

In England, for many centuries, the farmers were bound to the land, which was owned entirely by the aristocrats. These serf-farmers were compelled to yield portions of their produce and to give substantial periods of their time to their masters. Not until well into the 1700's did English farmers gain enough freedom to have an incentive for agricultural improvement, and thus to begin to assure the English of a steady food supply.

Dim though the records are, it is possible to show that the farmers—the food producers—in country after country, in century after century, were slaves or serfs or tenants, under conditions that discouraged all ambition and industry. Under feudalism, famine was inevitable whenever weather conditions were bad. Starvation for thousands of people, who were powerless to help themselves, was certain to follow.

Against this grim background rises the magnificent story of

Food in abundance at an American county fair.

H. Armstrong Roberts

farmers in America. Famine, starvation, or mass hunger have had no part in the history of the United States. Here, under a Constitution that has guaranteed all men the right to choose their occupations, those who have chosen to be farmers have provided their fellow countrymen with food in abundance. The efficiency which free farmers developed has not only fed our nation well; it has enabled millions who were not needed to raise food to work at the production of useful goods, luxuries, and services.

The story of free farmers is a story of plenty—plenty of food, and more of many desirable things than people anywhere at any time have ever enjoyed. The story carries with it a great promise of abundance for generations yet unborn, and a great obligation on the part of those alive today to keep our freedom.

CHAPTER 2

Furrows
across a Continent

The men who were to farm the wide new continent of America wanted to be able to build their homes on land that they owned. They came from countries where their ancestors had been lowly peasants, tenants, or even serfs bound to feudal lords. They and their forebears had dwelt in a caste society where few could rise, where custom reserved the ownership of land, with all it meant in security and prestige, to a privileged few. For the emigrant from the Old World, the chance to become possessor of a farm in his own name was a magical lure. The newcomer to America could see opportunity shining in his face from the western sun.

How were farmers to acquire the land they were to plow and own in this New World? There were many ways, and each has its story.

"An honest, valiant and industrious man," so Captain John Smith described William Spence, who became the first Englishman to own and operate an individual American farm. Spence, listed in the colony records as a laborer, arrived in the Jamestown, Virginia, colony during the winter of 1607–1608, but not until twelve long years had passed did he obtain his farm.

The struggling little settlement on the north bank of the James River was but a tiny pinpoint on the edge of a vast and unknown continental wilderness. Savage Indians, who knew no

8

reason to welcome the white-skinned intruders, kept the new-comers fearful. The London Company, to which King James of England had granted the right to settle Virginia, planned to run the colony on a communistic sort of plan. All the land belonged to the colony, rather than to individuals. Every man was supposed to work. Some had to build houses. Some had to guard against Indian attack or explore the nearby country. Some were ordered to raise crops. All the food produced was placed in a common storehouse, from which the officials portioned it out equally to all.

With little personal incentive, however, no one worked very hard. The crops, poorly cared for, yielded small harvests. Jamestown, as a result, was nearly starved out. If Captain John Smith had not traded with the Indians for corn, and if a ship had not brought new food supplies from England, the colony could have perished before it was well started.

Then, in 1611, the company sent out a new governor, Sir Thomas Dale. He saw the trouble at once. He abolished the communal plan. To each man he assigned three acres of land, and gave each the right to keep for himself most of what he raised. The result was amazing. Captain Smith wrote about it in his history:

When our people were fed out of the common store, and laboured jointly together, glad was he who could slip from his labour, or slumber over his taske he cared not how, nay, the most honest among them would hardly take so much true paines in a week, as now for themselves they will doe in a day: neither cared they for the increase, presuming that howsoever the harvest prospered, the generall store must maintaine them, so that wee reaped not so much Corne from the labours of thirtie, as now three or foure doe provide for themselves.

At last, in 1619, William Spence and several others were set free from service to the colony and, as Captain Smith wrote, "have chosen places to their content: so that now knowing their owne land, they strive who should exceed in building and planting."

As Virginia grew, any person who transported himself or

another person over the Atlantic was given fifty acres; grants of one hundred acres and more were freely made to many who, like Spence, had performed useful services to the colony. Men of influence and energy found ways to acquire larger tracts, which were tilled by slaves or by indentured servants. The indentured servants, after working a few years to repay the costs of their passage, were entitled to freeholds of their own.

The Mayflower group, and those who immediately followed it to Plymouth, Massachusetts, made the same mistakes as the Virginians. They, too, tried joint ownership of the land. Not enough work was done to feed the people. Those who did work faithfully complained that the shirkers got just as much as they did. After four years, Governor Bradford, by request of the colonists, assigned each family a piece of land at a distance from Plymouth, in addition to a town plot. For safety and defense, the people kept their homes and garden plots in the village. As the numbers grew—by 1750 Boston had 15,000 population and 180,000 had spread over Massachusetts—farmsteads were established, by allotment or purchase, from the Atlantic coast to the New York State line on the west.

Most of the land along the seaboard was first given to royal favorites or influential persons, who sold or sometimes gave it to emigrants who wanted to establish homes and farms. William Penn sold his rich lands in Pennsylvania to groups or individuals, but to those with means only to cross the Atlantic, he granted fifty acres for the low yearly rent of one penny an acre.

The red men, who occupied the continent when the Spanish and English explorers arrived, had neither surveyors nor courthouses. Moreover, the Christian kings of Europe blandly assumed that whenever their adventurers erected flags and crosses in the territories of "heathens and infidels," the land automatically became theirs to assign as they wished. The Indians believed that *they* owned the lands, although they had no concept of individual proprietorship. They viewed their tribal territories as communal areas over which to hunt, fish, and roam. Sometimes they were paid by the white man for their land, paid with trinkets or tools, guns, blankets or rum; at other times they were ruthlessly driven back by armed force; occasionally they were offered doles or pensions, and restricted to reservations. But, by whatever means, they were gradually displaced by the white man's superior force and irresistible determination.

In the seventeenth century, the English kings began granting vast tracts which reached vaguely westward, between specified northern and southern boundaries. The companies or proprietors who received these grants, in order to increase their useable wealth, then had to bring colonists, who would buy or rent their holdings and make the wilderness productive. Land was abundant—a whole continent full—and was worthless until human beings were ready to apply their labor to it.

Before the American Revolution, some 750,000 persons came to live in the thirteen colonies. Children were assets in an agricultural economy, because they could help with the work, and from generation to generation the population increased.

On that Thursday in April, 1789, when George Washington, the foremost farmer of his time, became the first President of the United States, nine out of every ten Americans were farmers. With the methods then known, the labors of nine were needed to feed ten. When Washington swore to "preserve, protect, and defend the Constitution of the United States," he assumed the leadership of a new nation that numbered fewer than four million people. These inhabitants were thinly scattered along the Atlantic coasts and rivers. Only a few of the most venturesome had pushed west of the Appalachian mountains.

Yet, within a century, American farmers had set their plows to turning up the virgin soil or were pasturing their growing herds in every fertile, watered region of the three-thousand-mile-wide continent.

Try to picture it: the stupendous feat of plowing a continent from coast to coast, a feat that was performed willingly and eagerly by multitudes of men, many of them strangers in a strange land. The toil was enormous. Difficulties and dangers, discouragements and disappointments confronted the plowmen nearly every step of the way. But no one forced the pioneers to cultivate the new lands. They were lured by the promise of better futures. The Constitution provided them with a government that left each man free to seek and enjoy the rewards his endeavors might earn. To become owners of land and to live as free and independent citizens, men faced incalculable perils in pursuit of the American dream.

The wilderness spread so far and wide that every individual who wished for land could have it; that seemed beyond doubt. Thomas Jefferson expected that a thousand years would pass before all the vacant lands could be occupied. He favored giving land to those who would build homes upon it and cultivate it. The ambitious farmer wanted title, legal and indisputable, to his acres.

When government under the Constitution was begun in 1789, the domain of the United States reached from the Atlantic to the Mississippi, except for Florida and a narrow strip along the Gulf of Mexico. By 1853, sixty-four years later, the Louisiana territory had been purchased from France, Florida had been acquired from Spain, the Republic of Texas had been annexed, California had been ceded by Mexico, the northwestern line had been fixed by treaty with England. The present continental boundaries of the nation were established. The whole United States was available to the plow. As a result, Congress was to wrestle for many decades with questions that had to do with the desires of men to develop and farm the billion fertile acres.

The itch to occupy the rich new lands, however, had not waited on the evolution of a nation. Early adventurers, who had scrambled over the mountain crests, liked what they saw beyond those Western slopes. The British king, George III, not wanting to stir up the Indians, decreed in 1763 that no settlements should be permitted farther west than the sources of the rivers that flowed to the Atlantic. But by 1769, a group had defied the King's order, and had settled on the Watauga River in Tennessee. Daniel Boone led North Carolinians to Kentucky in 1775.

Soldiers and officers of the Revolution received scrip certificates entitling them to tracts of Western land—everything beyond the Appalachians then was "West"—in acreages that varied with rank and length of service. One soldier was an exception. George Washington, who had declined any pay above his expenses for leading the armies, accepted no bounty of land. He did, however, own 32,373 acres in Ohio and West Virginia. For his services to the English crown during the French and Indian War, Governor Robert Dinwiddie of Virginia had awarded him 20,147 acres, and he had acquired more by purchase. Soldiers who did not want to move West sold their certificates to people who did, or to speculators, who bought land which they hoped to sell for a profit.

After the Revolution, most of the states ceded their Western claims to the federal government. Virginia kept an area in southwestern Ohio to reward her soldiers, and Connecticut for a time held on to an area in northeastern Ohio, which was called the Western Reserve.

The big westward rush really began in 1788. A group of New Englanders, for example, bought from Congress 1,500,000 acres in Ohio at the mouth of the Muskingum River, for considerations that in cash amounted to about eight cents an acre. In midwinter, forty-eight men, organized as the Ohio Company, set out from Ipswich, Massachusetts, and Hartford, Connecticut. To mark boundaries in the new land, build boats for transportation, to build houses and forge tools, four surveyors, six boat builders, four house carpenters, and a blacksmith were carefully included in the group. At the foot of the Tuscarora mountains in Pennsylvania, the deep snow forced them to abandon their wagons and build sleds. Upon reaching the Youghiogheny River, a tributary of the Monongahela, which joins the Allegheny to form the Ohio River in western Pennsylvania, a boat forty-five feet long, twelve feet wide, with bulletproof sides was built, along with flatboats and canoes. Five days later, the party landed at the mouth of the Muskingum and founded the town of Marietta.

During that same year, one historian says, eighteen thousand people from the Eastern states rafted down the Ohio River to settle in Ohio, Kentucky, and Indiana, and probably as many more tramped over the Southern mountain passes, chiefly through the Cumberlands where Virginia and Kentucky meet. Kentucky became a state in 1792, Tennessee in 1796, and Ohio in 1803.

With settlers pouring so rapidly into the wilderness, Congress had to decide between those who wanted the land to be given free to farmers and those who thought it ought to be sold. The national treasury needed money, so it was decided to sell. The first plan was to hold land auctions at the capital in Philadelphia (Washington after 1800), with a dollar an acre as the minimum price. Then, in 1796, the price was raised to two dollars, and buyers were given a year to pay. In 1800, credit was extended to four years. Plenty of land was sold, but it was difficult to collect the money from men who seldom saw hard cash. Finally, in 1820, a minimum of $1.25, payable in cash, was set, and that was the price until after 1862. Those who filled up the new states had to endure hard labor, risk the dangers of Indian attack, suffer disease without doctors, and spend long, lonely weeks without company.

A man, who now lives in a richly appointed Washington apartment and travels in important business circles, sometimes displays to his guests a strange-looking pocket compass, set in a folding, rectangular wooden frame. The compass belonged to John Carter, his great-great-grandfather. He tells how John Carter, in 1831, filed his claim on forty acres of rich black land four miles east of Bowling Green, now a county seat in northwestern Ohio. There, near the Portage River, he built a cabin, installed his family, and began clearing away the heavy trees so he could plant a garden and some grain. With a cow, pigs, and chickens, nuts and wild berries, and the game he could shoot, his young family was growing up strong and healthy.

Carter's problem was to earn some cash money. As yet there were no markets for anything he could raise, even if he produced beyond his needs. He had to have cash in order to pay the government the $1.25 an acre for his land, and he could get it in only one way: from the state of Ohio. The state paid bounties for wolf scalps, $2.50 for whelps and $4.50 for grown wolves. So time after time, Carter left his family alone in the isolated cabin while he ranged the deep forests, often staying away a week at a time. The grown wolves were wary, but now and then he was lucky enough to trace out a den of young. Finally, in 1836, he was able to set out on a twenty-mile walk to the courthouse at the then county seat in Perrysburg, where he received the bounty on enough wolf scalps to meet his need, and then to go to the land office and complete his payment. In time, there came a parchment deed, signed by President Andrew Jackson. John Carter at last owned his forty acres. The deed can still be seen, thanks to the care that John and his wife, Charity, took to preserve it. The compass? It had guided Carter week after week through the trackless woods, and steered his steps back home again. His gun and ax, adz and hoe have long been lost, but the compass links one twentieth-century American to his pioneer past.

The farm-hungry settlers did not always wait until the government surveyed the land and put it up for sale. Instead they built their cabins and started their clearings; then, if a speculator attempted to outbid them, trouble ensued. As a result, "Claims Associations" were organized to protect the occupant and see that he had to pay no more than the minimum of $1.25 to hold his claim. Finally, in 1841, Congress passed the Preemption Act, which gave the settler the first opportunity to buy the land he had started to develop.

Speculators, hopeful of large and quick profits, sought the most desirable lands, particularly in locations where towns might

develop. Some, whose judgments had been good and who persuaded farmers to buy, did very well. Others, like Daniel Webster,
who expected to get rich from unfortunate purchases in Illinois,
Michigan, and Wisconsin, were over-optimistic.

During the 1850's, one man bought 344,000 acres of Iowa
land. Public protest against such extensive speculation at last led
Congress to pass the Homestead Act. Under this law, signed
by Abraham Lincoln in 1862, any citizen, or an alien intending to
become a citizen, could become the owner, without payment,
of 160 acres, provided he made certain improvements and lived
upon the tract for five years.

Daniel Freeman, as the first homesteader, has earned a foot-
note in history. Born in Ohio and educated in Illinois as a physi-
cian, Freeman was a member of the United States secret service
during the Civil War. While on leave from duty at Fort Leaven-
worth, Kansas, he had spotted the claim he wanted, northwest of
Beatrice, Nebraska. On January 1, 1863, the day the new Homestead Law was to become effective, he was under orders to set out
for St. Louis. The land offices were to be closed on the New Year's
holiday, but Freeman persuaded the registrar of the land office to
open up for a few minutes after New Year's Eve. He became the
lucky holder of Homestead Certificate No. 1, Application No. 1,
and the pleased owner of the first free 160 acres. After the Civil
War, he lived on his farm until he died in 1908. Congress
has since made Freeman's 160 acres the Homestead National
Monument.

Besides the land that passed directly and indirectly to farmers
by way of homesteads, military bounties, cash sales, and private
claims, Congress gave millions of acres to the states for building
schools and colleges, for canals, drainage projects, and other inter-
nal improvements. Still more millions went free to corporations, to
help them build railroads. Altogether, 285 million acres were distributed as homesteads, 224 millions were granted to the states, 336
million were cash sales, 91 millions were railroad grants, and 95

A sod house was often the first shelter of the homesteader who took up land in the drier areas of the West. This one is more elaborate than most and has frame additions. Many has sod roofs as well as walls.

million acres were military bounties and private claims. The state and railroad lands, if they had agricultural value, were sold to farmers. Burlington railroad land in Iowa and Nebraska, for example, brought from four dollars to twelve dollars an acre. Finally, after the best lands were taken and it became plain that no one could make a living on only 160 acres of poorer land, particularly on the semi-arid western Great Plains, the Homestead Act was changed to increase the claim limit to 640-acre tracts.

Thus, less than thirty years after the Homestead Act was declared, nearly all the desirable land had been occupied. Or, only a hundred years after George Washington's inauguration day, the lure of land and freedom had, indeed, plowed the continent.

The Superintendent of Census wrote in his 1890 report: "Up to and including 1880 the country had a frontier of settlement, but at present . . . there can hardly be said to be a frontier line."

To most of us, a hundred years may seem a long time indeed, but in the perspective of history, a century, or even the longer period back to our national beginnings, is very brief. Try a quick exercise in simple arithmetic: From the present year subtract the year of Washington's inauguration, 1789, then divide by three. You can think of many a still-vigorous man no older than that! The span of three such brief lifetimes embraces the whole period during which the miracle of American growth has been accomplished.

Meanwhile, back in 1890, though the geographical frontier had been reached, the agricultural frontiers were still awaiting discovery.

CHAPTER 3

Farm Mechanics
Start a Revolution

Bowed by the weight of centuries he leans
Upon his hoe and gazes on the ground,
The emptiness of ages in his face,
And on his back the burden of the world.

—thus the late American poet Edwin Markham opens his famous poem, "The Man with the Hoe." And what he so movingly describes in these verses is indeed the way it had been for centuries with the man who tilled the earth, chained to backbreaking animal drudgery that made him "brother to the ox."

Plowing the earth is man's biggest job. To lift and turn the soil absorbs more energy than any other activity of humankind. For centuries, as we noted, farmers stirred the soil with hoes or mattocks or spades, as the Pilgrims did during their first years on these shores. Plows, when used, were no more than sharpened sticks, to which ingenious men eventually attached strips of metal to make them cut better and wear longer. Men and women, and later oxen and horses, pulled the plows.

Machinery multiplies the effect of energy; that is why it has been so important in American farming.

America's free farmers, with their own fields to plow, soon recognized the great need for machines that would make their labors more productive. The United States government promptly

19

offered an incentive to would-be inventors. Although burdened with the tremendous business of getting the new government under way, the first Congress took time, in 1790, to pass a patent law. Under this law, an inventor could deposit a description and model of his new device at the Patent Office. Once granted a patent, the inventor gained the exclusive right to make and sell his product for seventeen years. Unhappily, imitators often violated this right and compelled owners of patents to fight for protection in the courts.

In 1793, Thomas Jefferson, the farmer of Monticello, turned from his responsibilities as Secretary of State to design a new metal plow. By mathematical computations he tried to produce a moldboard—the curved iron plate which lifts and turns the soil—having the least possible resistance to the weight of the soil. Unfortunately, the mechanics he engaged failed to make the best of his design and the project was abandoned. Daniel Webster, another statesman, also designed a plow, a plow so massive that ten oxen were needed to pull it. Such heavy plows were not unusual. One man sometimes rode the beam which projected in front of the plow, to keep the point in the ground.

A cast-iron plow was patented in 1797 by Charles Newbold, a New Jersey farmer and mechanic, but unluckily for Newbold, a rumor that cast iron poisoned the soil made few farmers willing to risk its use. In 1819, a farmer from Cayuga County, New York, invented and patented the first really successful new type of cast-iron plow. The major sections were constructed in separate pieces, so the farmer who broke one part could replace it without having to buy a complete new plow. While Jethro Wood, the inventor, did not get rich, largely because others infringed on his patents, his plow design was widely used in the northeast, and early emigrants carried it westward to the prairies. A Virginia farmer, Stephen McCormick, also patented a plow with detachable parts, which he sold successfully in Virginia and other Southern states.

Nevertheless, the farmer who settled on the Midwestern

prairie lands had trouble with Jethro Wood's plow, and with all the other plows he used. He continually had to stop, yank his plow out of the furrow, and laboriously clean off the gluey earth with a wooden paddle. Unlike the looser, more pebbly soils of the East, the prairie earth was sticky. "We need a plow that scours," the farmers said over and over.

In Illinois, a country boy listened to the farmers' complaints. Back home in Vermont, John Deere had learned the blacksmith trade, and he had learned it well. He knew how to shoe horses and oxen; how to make good shovels, pitchforks, and manure forks; and how to hammer out parts for sawmills. A budding manufacturer, he had moved with his tool kit to Grand Detour in Illinois, where he saw an opportunity to make money if he could build a plow that would slide smoothly through the sticky prairie earth.

One day, at a nearby sawmill, he noticed a discarded circular saw blade of Sheffield steel. He carried it back to his shop and chiseled off the teeth. Then he made a plow model of wood, shaped as he thought the parts should be. Finally the smooth steel surface and rough wooden parts were finished, and Deere took the plow across the river where his friend, Lewis Crandall, owned a field. The ground was moist, but after cutting the first furrow, Deere lifted the plow to find the blade clean as a whistle. Again and again the plow cut into the wet, heavy earth, and always the blade emerged gleaming and free of dirt.

It was an historic morning. Never before had a plow scoured in such soil, pulled so easily, and turned so neat a furrow.

But John Deere was not satisfied. He thought he could strengthen the steel and improve the shape of the moldboard. The next year, 1838, he made three plows, and in 1839 ten plows. Three years later, surer of his product, he put together one hundred and peddled them by wagon to nearby farmers.

The inventor, enterprising and forward looking, now decided to become a manufacturer, who would provide good plows to all who wanted them. With some partners, he built a brick factory at

Grand Detour. At first, steel plates were shipped to him from England, but the cost was high and often the salt ocean air pitted the metal. Finally Deere went to a steel foundry in Pittsburgh, where he arranged to have steel rolled to his specifications. That year his factory turned out a thousand plows.

The fast-growing business convinced John Deere that he needed better ways of delivering his plows to the many places that wanted them. In 1847, he moved to Moline, on the Illinois bank of the Mississippi, so his merchandise could be shipped by water to the towns on the big river and its tributaries. Here, by 1852, he was making four thousand plows a year and could produce ten thousand. When the railroad came, in 1854, and the river was bridged near Moline, in 1856, he was ready to fill orders from anywhere in the United States.

Even before the new plows began to slice the prairie lands, two other inventions were making agricultural history.

One winter night, only three years after the patent law had been enacted, a tall, dignified young man, just past his twenty-seventh birthday, listened carefully, as a party of Georgia planters talked about their farming problems. They complained that it took a whole day's labor to separate a pound of cotton fiber from the seed, and asked why a machine couldn't do the work. The hostess, the widow of General Nathanael Greene, the Revolutionary War hero, was trying to make a living for herself and five children on the plantation that the state of Georgia, grateful for his military services, had given her husband. The young man was a Massachusetts farm boy, who had graduated from Yale College and gone to Georgia to be a tutor, only to find that his promised job had been given to someone else. Mrs. Greene, who met him on the boat from New York to Savannah, invited him to stay at her plantation until he could make new plans. Impressed by his ingenuity at fixing things around the plantation, she now suggested that perhaps he could make a machine to take the cotton from the seed.

A few weeks later, in April of 1793, Eli Whitney—the young

Yale graduate—invented a machine that was to change the future of the South. That machine was the cotton gin. With it, one worker could clean fifty pounds of cotton in a day. The consequences were tremendous. Cotton planting boomed across the entire South. Abundant cotton made abundant jobs in New England and British textile mills. Millions of people here and abroad wore better clothing.

Because his gin was easy to imitate, Whitney made little money from it. Back in Connecticut, he turned to manufacturing rifles for the government, and for his gunmaking initiated the principle of interchangeable parts, a development that led to the great mass-production industries of America.

Since biblical times, men, women, and children had stooped to harvest the world's cereal crops with a sickle. Through tens of centuries, no better tool had been devised for reaping than this curved knife with a small hand grip. Finally, some tall fellow, whose back hurt from bending day after day, invented the scythe, with its longer, heavier blade and long curved handle. Another genius attached a rack of wooden fingers parallel to the blade. The cradle, as this improvement was called, left the fallen grain in windrows, so that binding the sheaves was a little less wearisome. Even so, the binders had to bend low to gather up enough for a bundle, make a circlet of straw for a band, twist its ends into a firm knot, and set the bundle into a shock. Then the threshing had to be done with a flail.

The colonists brought the sickle and the cradle to America, and until the nineteenth century was almost half-gone, the nation's farmers found no better way to cut their wheat, oats, barley, rye, and rice.

Hand work was too hard and too slow to suit the ambitious farmers of the New World. The need for a reaping machine was plain, and several men with inventive minds worked on the problem. One of these men was Robert McCormick, a farmer-

The cradle preceded the reaper in the grain harvest. The cradled grain was gathered and tied by hand into bundles, and the bundles were set up in shocks to dry before threshing.

blacksmith from the upper Shenandoah Valley of Virginia, who made a sort of reaper as early as 1809. That same year, a son was born to the McCormicks, just three days after the Lincolns over in Kentucky had the new baby they called Abraham. The McCormicks named their little fellow Cyrus Hall.

Robert tinkered with ideas for a reaper, year after year. Meantime, he patented a blacksmith bellows, a gristmill, and other machines. Finally, however, he gave up his hopes of perfecting a reaper, after yet another new idea proved unworkable in 1831.

Cyrus, by then a vigorous young man, decided he would try to succeed where his father had failed. He had some new and different ideas. He hammered his parts into form at the family's forge. When they had been fitted together, he had included the important mechanical principles found in today's combine harvesters. The day came when the new contraption was to be tested in a wheat field. Curious neighbors left their work to watch.

The horses were hitched and the big main drive wheel turned the gears that moved the cutting knives. The severed stalks fell neatly onto the platform. The machine, crude though it was, did the job. Horsepower was finally to replace the muscles of men and women in the grain harvest. It was a great moment for young Cyrus McCormick. He could dream that one day thousands of reapers would be needed, and profits from making them would fill his pockets. Meanwhile, his mind was busy with ideas for improvements. He exhibited his machine, and demonstrated to skeptical farmers that it was practical.

When he was ready, in 1834, to take out patents, he found that a Yankee Quaker, Obed Hussey, had applied to patent a machine similar in many respects. Undiscouraged, McCormick kept working. In 1847, he built a factory in Chicago, and continued to improve his reaper. The patents ran out and renewal was refused in 1848, but the aggressive McCormick kept selling and expanding. He also kept fighting for his patents, and on one occasion the lawyer for his opponent was Abraham Lincoln. The world-famous International Harvester Company of today is built upon McCormick's beginnings.

The cotton gin, the reaper, and the steel plow—everyday tools of farming today—were revolutionary landmarks in the perspective of agricultural history. They not only helped enormously to make the energies of farmers more effective, but inspired hundred of farmers, blacksmiths, and tinkerers all over the United States to try to devise other machines to do work easier, faster, and better. Always they saw the chance to harvest profits from royalties, as well as crops, if their inventions or improvements could be patented and sold widely.

The flail with which farmers beat the grain from the straw was as slow and inadequate as the sickle had been for use in the fields. George Washington had corresponded with English agriculturists about a threshing machine, and Thomas Jefferson had tinkered with one. But not until 1837 was a practical thresher patented. A horse walking on a treadmill provided the power. Later improvements led to sweep-power threshers, worked by horses driven in a circle.

By 1841, someone patented a grain drill to replace the ancient method of planting seeds broadcast by hand. In 1873, a reaper, which bound sheaves with wire, came on the market, soon to be replaced by the twine binder. And by the end of the century, huge combine harvesters, drawn by multiple teams of horses, had appeared in the grain fields on the Pacific coast.

So, as the American dream of a better life kept pushing men forward, the land hummed from coast to coast with the stepped-up activity of America's farmers.

For half a century, roughly 1880 to 1930, this scene was typical of grain-threshing time in the Middle West. The bundles were brought from the field on wagons and pitched to the separator, which here is hidden behind a loaded wagon. The steam traction engine provided the power. Straw passed through the blower at the rear.

U.S.D.A. photo

CHAPTER 4

Crops
Farmers Grow

The earliest tribes of mankind were "gatherers." They ate what they could find or catch: shellfish, nuts, berries, roots, birds' eggs, and wild animals. Later, though still long before recorded history, their primitive successors learned to tame animals and plant crops. When did actual farming begin? The archeologists, who try to solve the riddles of man's past, are unable to say.

Wheat probably was first cultivated in Asia Minor. Grains of it, harvested four or five thousand years ago, have been found in Egypt's ancient tombs. Wheat, barley, rye, flax, oats, and common fruits and vegetables were well known in Europe many centuries before the New World was discovered. Yet, because no records were kept, botanists have had to guess whether certain vegetables, grasses, and other kinds of plants are native to the Old World or to the New.

Adventurers who followed Columbus to the New World— Spanish, Portuguese, English, Dutch, Italian, French—cruised up and down the coasts of North and South America. Settlements were established in the West Indies. Cortes conquered Mexico, and Spanish expeditions wandered as far north as Kansas. French and English fishing ships came to Newfoundland and Labrador, where their crews went ashore to dry and salt their catches.

Seeds went along with all these early travelers, in the food

27

supplies they brought, in the straw of their bedding, perhaps in other ways. Thus, by intent or accident, new plants sprouted on American soil around the explorers' camps. The Indians adopted some of the species whose products they liked, and so the plants began to spread. The explorers, naturally, were intensely curious about the strange plants they found growing in an unknown land, and they took samples home with them. Thus, within a few decades, new species were not only brought to the New World, but plants native to the Americas were carried by traders on their voyages along the coasts of Europe, Africa, the Near East, and India.

No question exists about the origin of one important plant: corn. Christopher Columbus, reporting on his first voyage to America, wrote of "a sort of grain the Indians call maize, which was well tasted, baked or dried, and made into flour." Later explorers found maize in cultivation from Peru to Canada.

Nor is there any doubt that tobacco originated in the New World. In the journal of his 1492 voyage, Columbus told about "men and women with a half-burnt weed in their hands, being the herbs they are accustomed to smoke." In 1535, the French explorer, Jacques Cartier, saw Indians along the St. Lawrence River smoking tobacco in "a hollow piece of stone or wood like a pipe."

In the middle of the sixteenth century, Spaniards began shipping the tobacco leaf from their West Indian colonies. The demand grew rapidly, first among the aristocrats who made smoking a fashionable novelty, and then among other classes of people. Some Europeans believed smoking to be good for the health; others felt it detrimental. King James I of England was one of those who found tobacco objectionable, and in 1604 wrote and published anonymously his *Counterblaste to Tobacco*. Nevertheless, he was willing to accept the taxes levied on tobacco imports.

In 1612, John Rolfe, best remembered for his marriage to Chief Powhatan's daughter, Pocahontas, began to cultivate tobacco at Jamestown, Virginia. He considered the native Indian tobacco inferior, so by experimentation, and perhaps by obtaining better seed from the West Indies, he learned how to produce a superior leaf. Thus, tobacco quickly became the first agricultural product to be exported in quantity from the new English colony. From the proceeds of its sale in England, the Virginians bought clothing, tools, ammunition, and other necessities. So swiftly did the profits rise that by 1616 even the streets and the market place of Jamestown were planted in tobacco. In fact, for nearly two hundred years tobacco stood first among American exports; not until 1803, after the gin had multiplied the cotton output, did it drop to second position.

The fortunes of the Virginia and Maryland tobacco farmers, during colonial times, fluctuated sharply. They were required to ship their output to England in English ships. Export taxes were exacted at home to help support the colonial governments, and heavy import taxes were imposed in England to enrich the royal treasury. With their market so far away, planters faced constant uncertainty; and often a new crop was set out before they heard what the previous one had earned. Prosperous years led to overproduction, and the surpluses in turn brought about laws to restrict the amount planted. Serious, though unsuccessful, efforts were even initiated to prohibit all tobacco production for one year.

Meanwhile, the British government decided that it also wanted to obtain silk, wine, and flax from Virginia, instead of having to pay other countries for these commodities. Decrees were issued, requiring each farmer to set out mulberry trees, raise silkworms to feed on them, and to plant grape vines and flax. The plan failed, for the soils and climate were not suited to such crops, and the farmers soon began again to plant the tobacco from which they could make the most money.

All countries where tobacco was grown or traded made it a source of taxes. In France and other nations, the importation and sale of tobacco were monopolized by the government. Benjamin Franklin helped to finance the American Revolution by borrowing two million livres, to be repaid to France by five million pounds of best Virginia leaf. (Tobacco taxes nowadays return three billion dollars

Tobacco being cultivated and side-dressed with potash and nitrogen on a field at the U.S. Department of Agriculture Beltsville Research Center in Maryland.

a year to the United States federal, state, and municipal treasuries, three times the amount the tobacco farmers receive.)

Less than one-half of one per cent of United States crop land is now planted in tobacco. Of the eighteen states which cultivate the crop, the Carolinas, Kentucky, Virginia, Tennessee, and Georgia produce the most.

Compared to tobacco's small acreage, corn is planted each year on nearly twenty per cent of our cultivated land. No plant has meant so much to America. For the Incas of Peru, for the Mayans and Aztecs of Guatemala and Mexico, and for most of the Indian tribes of what is now the United States, corn was a staple food. Today, corn is the basic animal feed in America's tremendous meat industry. Like tobacco, corn depends wholly on the care of man for its survival; it doesn't grow wild, and if the seed were not saved and planted, corn would become extinct.

Every month of the year sees a corn harvest somewhere, as far south as Venezuela, as far north as Canada, below sea level on the Kazakhstan plain in Russia, or two miles high in the Andes. Corn is grown in more than fifty countries, but nowhere is it produced so abundantly as in the Corn Belt of the central United States.

An adaptable plant, corn made its way around the world even faster than tobacco. It was known in China by 1573. In the early 1600's when Captain John Smith cruised up the James River and into Chesapeake Bay, he traded with the Indians for corn to bolster the food supplies of the famished Virginia colonists. Later, with advice from Indian captives, the settlers learned to grow their own corn. When the Mayflower colonists landed, they rejoiced to find a heap of corn which the Indians had covered with woven mats and earth, and helped themselves. Then the friendly Indian, Squanto, who had lived in England and who spoke the language, showed them how to plant the hills at four-foot intervals, with a fish in each hill for fertilizer, and made them wait until the proper time in May to begin planting.

From Jamestown to Plymouth, corn nourished the settlement

of the continent. Wherever men girdled trees to start a clearing in the forest, corn was planted; wherever they pushed out into the tough sods of the open prairies, corn went with them. With corn bread, their families could eat. If the family had a cow, as well, there was nourishing mush and milk. Given fair conditions, the vigorous plant seldom failed to grow and produce. The poorest settler, who carried little more than an ax, a gun, and a hoe could, with a sack of seed corn, be on his way toward becoming a farmer and landowner.

When tombs five thousand years old were opened recently in India, there was cotton in them. Ancient Chinese and ancient Egyptians knew cotton. Cotton cloth was woven in Peru before 1200 A.D., when the Incas rose to power; and remains of fabric in Arizona's thousand-year-old pueblo ruins disclose that cotton was known to their builders. This plant, which American farmers have produced almost since the nation began, traces its origins to both the Old and New Worlds, and grows in many species and varieties.

The value of cotton lies in the fiber which covers the seeds. Each fiber is shaped like a flattened tube, and its unique spiral twist gives it an elastic quality that permits it to be spun and woven into many kinds of fabrics.

Southern colonists began early to experiment with cotton, but not until 1746, after seeds of Asian varieties were obtained, did the crop begin to show promise. By the time the Revolutionary War ended, new spinning machinery and looms had been invented in England, and the mills there were eager to buy American cotton. However, the slow process of picking the lint from the seed kept the output low, until Whitney invented the gin. Then, within ten years, exports leaped two-hundred fold, and "King Cotton" ruled the South. From Georgia and the Carolinas, cotton moved northward into Virginia and into the new lands of Alabama and Mississippi. It became the important crop of Arkansas, Texas, and Oklahoma; and later, of California.

Until recent years, cotton required many hours of labor to plant, cultivate, and harvest. After the young plants appeared, the rows had to be thinned, hoed repeatedly, and cultivated with a one-horse or one-mule implement. Harvesting meant going over the field two or three times, to pluck the ripe fibers from the bolls in which they grew. For all this, planters found Negro slave labor profitable. When the Confederate states seceded and the Civil War ensued, Southern leaders expected England to help them because her mills needed raw cotton, but they were to be disappointed. Not only was much English sentiment opposed to slavery, but England did not want to lose its wheat supply from the North. Thus two great farm crops played a pivotal role in that tragic period of American history.

The most spectacular story about the crops grown by American farmers concerns the soybean. This story took a long time to unfold. In 2838 B.C., the Chinese Emperor Shennung wrote a book about useful plants, which told of the soybean's merit as food and medicine. Specimens were known in Europe around 1750. The American captain of a Yankee clipper ship, trading along the China coast in 1804, tossed a few bags of soybeans into the ship's hold, to insure an emergency food supply for the long sail home. Whether the crew ate any no one knows; at least some of the beans remained to be planted in American soil. Commodore Perry brought two varieties back from Japan in 1854, but no one foresaw their future as a billion-dollar crop. The soybean long remained a mere botanical curiosity in the United States as in Europe.

It was not until a whole century after the Yankee clipper's hold was emptied that American farm scientists began to find values in the soybean and to experiment with different varieties. Venturesome farmers tried them for hay, and found that cattle and sheep relished the dried vines. Hogs liked the beans, which nature filled with protein and oils. By 1920, a million bushels were harvested.

Forty years later the soybean crop was five hundred times greater—more than five hundred million bushels. What had caused so great a leap? The true answer may be found in the freedom of America's farm and industrial enterprises, which took advantage of new opportunities. The beans were not only used for hay, but planted in cornfields to be "hogged down" (meaning that hogs fed on both corn and beans), thus the demand for seed rose rapidly. Meanwhile, processors tried to make a profit by extracting the oil, which they could sell readily, and separating the meal which remained. The meal was rich in protein and proved to be excellent for livestock, though farmers at first regarded its use with suspicion. Fearing the seed demand would collapse from overexpansion, farmers increased their production slowly; the processors who envisioned a large potential market for the oil in margarine and cooking compounds and for the meal as livestock feed could not buy enough beans to build up the volume they needed for economical operation. Then, in 1928, three industrial leaders got together on the problem. One was head of a large Illinois feed-milling company, another of a major Eastern feed-distributing coöperative, the third was an Illinois seedsman who also had started to process soybeans. They announced that they would contract to buy, at a stipulated minimum price, all the soybeans that could be produced on fifty thousand acres. As a result, that year farmers harvested nearly eight million bushels.

The harvesting problem, however, still troubled farmers. To cut the vines with a binder, set the bundles up to dry in small shocks, and then to haul and run them through a threshing machine was expensive and laborious. They needed a combine harvester, adjusted for soybeans. The combine method of cutting and threshing wheat and oats had been slowly spreading eastward from the West's big grain farms, as better machines were devised. The manufacturers soon produced a combine harvester adapted to the smaller Midwestern and Eastern farms, which threshed not only wheat and oats but did an excellent job with soybeans as well.

Soybeans in a contoured field.

Now, with an assured market and economical harvesting equipment, soybean farmers expanded their acreage. They welcomed a new crop, which year after year brought a good price while overabundant corn and oats were becoming surpluses.

Scientists and salesmen worked to see that the demand for soybeans kept pace with booming production, and did it successfully. They learned how to improve the oil for use as a shortening, in margarine, and in salad dressing; and how to treat it for use in paints, lubricants, and printing inks. They sold the meal mainly as a protein ingredient for animal and poultry feed. Both oil and meal have yielded an amazing variety of products, from adhesives and paper coatings to fire-fighting foam and emulsifiers. At least five hundred different consumer products owe something to soybeans.

From the small beginning a few decades ago, farmers have increased plantings until now soybeans are the fifth biggest money-making crop in the United States. Corn is the biggest of all; then wheat, hay, and cotton; tobacco is sixth. Although these six account for two-thirds of the twenty billion dollars worth of crops farmers harvest each year, more than two hundred other crops are grown.

Our 180 million people demand all sorts of things. Parsley might seem to be a trivial and insignificant item; yet it would take a freight train more than one hundred cars long to haul all the parsley that one large city, Philadelphia, buys in a year. If you were to stroll through the aisles of your nearest supermarket, you would quickly realize that farmers do a really varied business, as you note the apples, apricots and almonds, cabbage, carrots and cucumbers, potatoes and peaches, prunes and pecans, lettuce and tomatoes, walnuts and watermelons, to mention only a few. Some of these, the prunes and almonds for instance, come from a few thousand acres in California; others, such as potatoes and tomatoes, grow in each state. The United States has nearly every combination of soil, rainfall, temperature, and altitude needed for the cultivation of almost all useful plants, except those which require strictly tropical conditions. If there are enough people who will buy a crop, farmers somewhere in the country will try to grow it.

CHAPTER 5

Animals
that Serve Man

Long centuries before human beings began to set down written records, horses, cattle, sheep, hogs, and goats had become domestic animals in southern and eastern Asia and around the Mediterranean Sea. Chickens, ducks, and geese were common fowls before the Christian era. People, in those distant times, liked not only grains, fruits, and vegetables, but also meat and eggs, as well as people do now. The turkey, an American bird, was well known in Europe, before the English settled on the Atlantic Coast; it is believed to have been tamed by some Indian tribes in our Southwest. With this possible exception, every farm animal in either the New or the Old World was domesticated before men learned to write.

The aboriginal Indians in North America kept no livestock. The dog, which seems to have accompanied their ancestors, who are supposed to have come by way of the Bering Strait from Asia, was their only domesticated animal. For meat, they killed or trapped wild animals and caught fish.

It was the Spaniards and other early explorers who brought horses, hogs, cattle, sheep, and goats to this continent. At sea for two or three months at a time—Columbus took seventy-one days for his first voyage—they needed fresh meat now and then. Though the ships were seldom more than one hundred feet long, there was always room for a few animals. Some of the livestock was kept for breeding purposes, when settlements were established, while horses were brought for transportation and to ride into battle against the Indians.

From time to time horses and cattle escaped from the camps of the explorers and from the ranches the Spaniards established in Mexico. The wild horses—called mustang, bronco, or cayuse— which by tens of thousands once roamed parts of the West, were descended from these Spanish horses. They became the mounts of the Western Indians, and they were also caught and broken for farm and ranch use.

When Hernando De Soto and his men landed in Florida in 1539 to look for gold, they brought thirteen sows with them. The Spaniards' search for gold was fruitless, but by the time De Soto was buried in the Mississippi's muddy waters, nearly four years later, the hogs were said to have numbered several hundred. These were ancestors of the razorback swine which, until well into the twentieth century, were famous in the Gulf states.

Animals were not pampered in colonial times. Little shelter was provided, and in winter cattle, hogs, and sheep had to forage as best they could, while in summer they ate new grass. Horses received the best care, because most travel was by horseback. When racing became a popular sport, that, too, led to better attention and feeding for the horses.

"Three heifers and a bull, the first beginning of any cattle of that kind in the land," Governor Bradford of Plymouth wrote in 1624, referring to the first precious livestock in his colony. Thirty cows, along with several mares, hogs, and goats, were unloaded at the wharf in Boston six years later, for the colonists there. Gradually, by importation and natural increase, livestock grew in numbers. In 1646, a summer visitor to Boston's fifty-acre Common could have counted seventy milk cows grazing. The Common had been set apart in 1634 as " a trayning field and for the feeding of cattell," and continued to be used as a pasture, often with soldiers drilling nearby, until 1829. (Ticket holders could pasture one cow or four sheep.) New England villages not only provided "commons" for milk cows, but often hired a "cow keeper," whose summer job was to guard the livestock while they pastured on meadows in the countryside nearby. Along the ocean, small peninsulas, jutting into the water, were fenced off, thus easily confining the animals at small expense. In the Southern colonies, much of the stock was permitted to roam freely in the woods.

The livestock in those days bore small resemblance to the fine animals seen on American farms today. The cattle were shaggy and small, the hogs generally scrawny, and the sheep inferior. Well-defined breeds, such as Jerseys or Herefords, were unknown. The only restrictions on breeding were vague laws, requiring that only bulls approved as "best" be permitted on the public pastures; nor were cattle specialized as they are now. A cow might be expected to give milk, work in harness, and when her useful days were over, be killed to supply meat and leather. In time, certain cattle were selected and bred for ability to give milk; others were trained as oxen to pull wagons, plows, and farm implements. Thousands of

The ox as a draft animal has almost disappeared from the United States farm. In the background, a team is hitched to an ox cart. The young man in the foreground demonstrates both that he is "on his rocker" and that the animal has a broad back.

the wagons, which carried nineteenth-century families and their freight to the West, were drawn by these sturdy oxen.

Improved strains of farm animals were imported from England and Europe by American farmers from time to time after the Revolutionary War, but not until well into the nineteenth century did farmers begin to adopt and develop specialized breeds.

Merino sheep led the parade of purebred livestock to America, but centuries of distinction among sheep had preceded the Merino's arrival here. More than a thousand years ago, Spain was known for its beautiful textiles woven from the fine native wool of Merino sheep. The demand for Spanish-made wool and cloth was so great and the trade so profitable that the rulers of Spain strictly forbade the sale of the sheep outside the country. The great flocks, sometimes numbering thirty thousand, were owned by the kings, the nobility, and the clergy. In winter, shepherds drove the flocks to the mild climate of southern Spain. In spring, as soon as the newborn lambs were able to travel, the flocks returned to the greener pastures of the north. Thus the mistaken belief arose that the best wool grew on sheep which were kept moving.

The story of how Merinos first came to the United States is a colorful and adventurous one. In 1796, Colonel David Humphreys, long a close friend of General Washington and once his military aide, was made United States minister to Spain. Colonel Humphreys was also a farmer, and was well informed about the marvelous qualities of the Merino sheep. When his term of office expired and he got ready to return to the United States, he determined to take home something that would bring lasting benefit to his country. The export of sheep from Spain was illegal, but controls were lax, and Humphreys managed, without getting into trouble, to smuggle seventy-five ewes and twenty-five rams over the border into Portugal. He piled all of them aboard a ship and transported them safely across the Atlantic to his farm in Derby, Connecticut. He is said to have sold choice sheep later for as much as $1,000 and $1,500 apiece.

On a headstone in a cemetery at Weathersfield, Vermont, the likeness of a sheep is carved. The design commemorates the work of William Jarvis, a Boston-born businessman, who in his later years farmed at Weathersfield and died there. From 1802 to 1811, Jarvis served as United States consul at Lisbon. After Napoleon conquered Spain in 1808, and relaxed the laws against exporting sheep, Jarvis shipped almost four thousand Merinos to various American ports. Other shiploads followed. The wool business boomed during the War of 1812. After the peace profits declined, but the Merinos remained. New England and then Ohio became centers for their breeding. Then, as settlements moved westward, the sheep moved too, eventually becoming the most abundant breed on the Western plains and mountains.

The dominant Western type is a large Merino, the Rambouillet, developed in France from a flock that originally belonged to King Louis XVI. Another American diplomat, Robert R. Livingston, who in 1803 helped buy Louisiana from France, brought the first of these Rambouillets to his large estate, Clermont, on the Hudson River.

The characteristic which made the Merino valuable on the Western ranges can be traced to the Spanish custom of keeping the flocks moving. The breed acquired the instinct of gregariousness; individual sheep do not wander far from their flock. In this, they differ from sheep of the English breeds, accustomed to centuries of enclosure within fences and hedges and thus to the habit of scattering about.

During the nineteenth century, enterprising farmers began to import British sheep. Grown more for their mutton than for their wool, these breeds had developed in various parts of the British Isles. Southdown, Shropshire, Hampshire, Dorset, Cheviot, Oxford, and Suffolk, each with distinctive characteristics, are the best-known names. Ranchmen, who wanted a sheep that produced both a good weight of mutton and of wool and that could adapt to rugged range conditions, crossed long-wooled British animals with the Rambouillet, and obtained the principal new breed created in the United States. They named it the Columbia.

The importers of purebred sheep, cattle, and horses tried to get the finest specimens from families of animals which had a proven ability to pass on good qualities. The best of the offspring were exhibited at fairs and livestock expositions and widely advertised. Other farmers, anxious to improve their own flocks, purchased sires and dams from these new lines. Thus the free movement of champion-quality animals has, in a few decades, provided the United States with herds and flocks which can be fed economically and which, in turn, produce profitably for their owners.

In 1837, Henry Clay, the famous Kentucky statesman, wrote to his agent in New York about some overseas "travelers" then on their way to Ashland, his farm at Lexington. He gave detailed instructions for their care and asked that they be routed by way of the Erie and Ohio canals, so that "these Portuguese dignitaries" would have a comfortable trip. The "Portuguese dignitaries" were four red pigs. Clay often bought animals from abroad, as did his friend Daniel Webster.

Unlike most of the sheep and all but one of the cattle breeds, the popular hog breeds were shaped by American farmers. The red Durocs, the Chester Whites, the Poland Chinas, and the picturesque Hampshires—black hogs with white shoulder belts—owe their characteristics to the work of breeders in this country.

Fashions affect the breeding of livestock, just as they do the styles of clothing or automobiles, though the changes are less abrupt. Fifty years ago, the most popular hogs were short-legged, round, and chubby. After World War I, breeders began to lengthen the legs so hogs could range more easily. Until about 1930, lard sold well both in the United States and abroad, so big, fat hogs paid well. Then the demand for lard began to decline; effort was turned toward producing a leaner hog, one that grew to market weight and condition in six months or less. The "ton-litter"

U.S.D.A. photo

A herd of Herefords luxuriate in a brome grass and alfalfa pasture on an Illinois farm.

became a goal—sows that would produce a litter that weighed two thousand pounds within six months.

Breeders of beef cattle aimed for a "meat-type" steer, which grew quickly to market quality within a minimum of fat meat. The main effort nowadays is to breed animals which most economically convert pasture and feedstuffs into quality meat, and which return the best profits to their owners.

The three best-known breeds of beef cattle all had their origins in Great Britain. These are the red, white, and roan Shorthorn; the red-coated, white-faced Hereford; and the all-black Aberdeen Angus. The sacred cattle of India, known as Brahmans, have also won an important place in the American beef industry, because they don't mind the heat of the South. They are usually silver gray in color and distinguished by the shoulder hump, drooping ears, and uprising horns. Brahman and Shorthorn blood was combined in the only strictly American beef breed. This is the

Santa Gertrudis, a splendid all-red animal, developed on the million-acre King Ranch near Corpus Christi, Texas.

In order to supply the tremendous demand of Americans for milk, butter, cheese, ice cream, and other dairy products, farmers have worked to improve the productivity of their cows for a hundred years. The first step, after the idea of a specialized dairy industry had evolved, was to bring from Europe the best milking animals known there. From the north of Holland came the big black-and-white Holsteins, from the Channel Islands the Jerseys and Guernseys. The hardy Brown Swiss were brought from the valleys of Switzerland, and the colorful Ayrshires from the southwest of Scotland. These five breeds produce most of the nearly sixty billion quarts of milk that Americans use up each year.

Most of the "pure" breeds of livestock trace their origins to localities where, sometimes through several centuries, the farmers preferred to develop animals with specific characteristics. Eventually, in order to preserve the inherited qualities and to make sure that no strange or inferior blood could affect the offspring, associations of breeders were formed and "herd books" established. Only animals whose ancestry could be proven and whose characteristics met breed standards could be registered in the herd books. Today every cattle breed of commercial importance in the United States has its association and its herd book.

For more than three centuries the horse played a major role in the daily life of the American farmer. The horse shared with oxen the labor of pulling the plow and harrow, and after the paths became roads, he pulled the carts, buggies, and coaches. Tramping on the wooden boards of a treadmill or walking an endless circle, he turned the wheels of crude threshing machines. In the West, he and the cowboy handled the cattle. In 1915, American farms counted more than 21,000,000 horses and mules. Today the figure stands below three million.

Until the low-priced automobile took over in 1910, first the riding horse and then the road horse transported farmers from home to town and on errands about the countryside. After the middle of the nineteenth century, the buggy became the almost universal vehicle for family transportation. Designed with a light frame attached to four high steel-rimmed wheels, the buggy was an easy load for one horse to pull. Farmers with large families used two-seated surreys, to which two horses were harnessed. Just as people take pride in their shining automobiles now, farmers took pride in the well-groomed road horses which carried them along at five or six miles an hour. The fastest horses provided popular sport at county-fair racing events, and horses were often bred for speed. The favorite, however, was the gentle, steady horse, which any member of the family could drive safely and children could ride or drive to school.

The road horse was too light in muscle and weight for the hard work of the fields. To furnish field power, farmers needed animals that were broad of back, strong of muscle, and heavy enough to pull a deepset plow or a well-loaded wagon. The demand for heavier, stronger horses led importers to bring from France the big Percherons, and from Belgium the sturdy Belgians, massive

A well-matched team of Belgian draft horses in Aroostook County, Maine.

horses, which weighed a ton or more. Less popular on farms, but splendid for pulling heavy drays and trucks on city streets, were the handsome Clydesdales from Scotland and Shires from England. Crossed with sires from these breeds, the lighter horses produced offspring weighing 1,400 pounds and more. Much of the continent's farm land was plowed year after year by such teams.

The cowboy needed still another kind of horse. He wanted a tough, wiry animal that could carry him all day in the saddle, capable of bursts of speed when cutting a steer out from a herd, strong of legs, and intelligent enough to stop quickly when the lariat found its mark. Ranchmen continuously selected the choice steeds, until eventually the American quarter horse was well-defined as a special breed.

Still another breed suited the requirements of the Southern plantation owner who moved from field to field, covering many miles in a day's work. His choice was the Tennessee walking horse. Easy to ride, it could move at a smooth walk, a running walk, or gentle canter. In the Southern states, mules were long preferred to horses for the share-crop cultivation of cotton, tobacco, and peanuts. The mule is produced by mating a male donkey with a female horse. A hybrid, unable to reproduce itself, the mule has been ridiculed as "without pride of ancestry nor hope of posterity." Nevertheless, it is a tough, economical, and sensible animal, admirably adapted for many uses. It became well known in the South after George Washington, in 1787, was presented with a fine jack by the king of Spain. Forty years later, Henry Clay brought another from Malta. The descendants of these and other famous jacks, brought from abroad, turned Southern soil for more than a century.

CHAPTER 6

When Muscles
Were in Power

Spencer Logan, in 1901, owned a medium-sized Midwestern farm of 125 acres. The neighbors looked upon this tall, quiet man with his bronzed countenance and gray, close-cropped mustache as a good model to follow. He was neither the first nor the last to buy a new kind of machine or to plant a new kind of corn, and when he made a change, they could be sure he had carefully investigated its worth. He was, they knew, an efficient and progressive farmer.

Born in 1851, Spencer could remember when his father's log house was lighted at night with homemade tallow candles. He remembered when many farmers harvested their wheat with cradles and tied the bundles with bands of straw. From his boyhood home, he had saved a flail that his father had used to thresh out grain on the barn floor. He had helped with horsepower threshing machines before the traction engine came on the scene. As a boy, he had planted corn by dropping seeds and pushing the earth over them with his bare feet.

Spencer was a link to the agricultural past, to the years when farming methods and implements still differed little from those of centuries long gone. During his lifetime, more improved equipment and methods had been developed than during the previous five thousand years. The new century was to bring greater changes.

They appeared, one after another, in different agricultural areas.

Not until near the middle of the 1900's did the full force of agricultural revolution become apparent. Spencer was to live long enough to see it build up, but not long enough to witness the tremendous transition from muscle power to engine power, nor the spectacular march of science into agriculture. Before he retired, Spencer acquired many new pieces of mechanical equipment, and, in 1912, he bought his first automobile. The tractor, the motor truck, the electric motor came into common use after his time.

The Logans felt that they were living well in 1901. After his years as a hired man and as a renter, Spencer now had paid for his farm and built a fine new barn. He had just moved into a new nine-room frame house, equipped with a bathroom and a hot-water furnace. The rural delivery brought his mail daily, and a telephone connected him with his neighbors and the nearest town. A hired man and his wife moved into the old house; Mrs. Logan no longer had to cook and keep house for field help.

The year-around work force included Spencer, the hired man, and, when school was not in session, Spencer's son Jimmy. Their muscles, two teams of draft horses, and a driving horse did the work. A windmill pumped water; at threshing time Spencer hired a steam-threshing outfit.

As soon as the soil was dry enough in the spring, Spencer started the plowing. This meant moving and turning hundreds of tons of earth. In a ten-hour day, a man and team could plow about two acres. If one man had thirty acres to plow by himself, he walked back and forth across his fields between the plow handles for fifteen full days.

The field work began at seven in the morning and did not end until six in the evening, with only an hour's break at noon for dinner. The horses could work no longer than this. The chores, feeding the livestock and milking the cows, were done before and after the long hours in the field.

"Jimmy, how about taking the harrow, now that school's

A wooden windmill of the type used on Spencer Logan's farm.

out?" Spencer asked one Saturday morning in late April. The one-room district school ran only seven months, from early October to April. The harrow, with its strong steel teeth, was easy enough to manage. Jimmy felt very proud, as he guided the team over the freshly plowed ground, while the harrow broke up the clods and fitted the surface for planting seed. After the plowing and harrowing was finished, Jimmy rode the heavy iron roller which smoothed the surface and broke the soil into still finer particles.

Then Spencer hitched the fastest walking team to the two-row planter, driving carefully to make the rows as straight as possible. With three days of good weather, the corn planting was done. The season's work, though, was only begun. As soon as the shoots of green young corn appeared above ground, Jimmy harrowed the fields again, exposing to the hot sun the sprouts of innumerable weeds which, if left to grow, would ruin the corn.

After the final harrowing, the cultivators took over. These were light, high-wheeled machines, under which two gangs of small shovels were suspended. Spencer rode one cultivator and the hired man the other. Three times, before the stalks grew too high in early July, they cultivated the corn, row by row. Jimmy followed on foot with a hoe, chopping out weeds the cultivators missed and straightening up small cornstalks that were accidentally covered with earth.

"Until about twenty years ago," Spencer told Jimmy, "no one thought about putting a seat on the cultivator. We used to cultivate corn with a small walking plow that took two trips for each row."

If everything went well, the corn was "knee high by the Fourth of July," and the cultivators were put away. The corn was "laid by," it was said. Unless too many weeds sprang up in July and August, the corn field work was over for a few weeks.

The cultivating was seldom finished before the hay was ready to harvest. With one team hitched to the mower, Spencer cut a few acres each morning and left the green clover to dry in the sun. On the second or third morning, he stirred the earlier cuttings with a tedder, a machine which kicked the hay into the air and left it to fall loosely so that it would dry faster.

Then, once the hay was dry, Jimmy hitched the driving horse to a wide steel rake, and gathered it into windrows. Spencer and the hired man followed with a flat-topped wagon. Sometimes Spencer hired additional help during the busy harvest weeks. The men lifted hay to the wagon with pitchforks, until the pile was so high they could reach no higher. As they pitched the hay, Spencer carefully arranged it into a square load, well-balanced so that it could not fall off. Then the wagon, heavy with sweet-smelling hay, was driven to the barn where it was unloaded. With ropes, pulleys, and a special big hayfork, the hay was lifted to the top of the barn and dropped into the roomy mows. The men pushed it tightly into place, so that no space was wasted. The haymaking took two weeks of hard, and often hot, work.

June, July, and August were months of hurry. Corn cultivation overlapped haymaking time, and haymaking overlapped the wheat harvest. No sooner was the hay in the barn, than the three stoutest horses were harnessed to the binder. The binder mowed the standing grain and tied it into bundles. Then came a tiring job for the two men who picked up the bundles, set ten of them firmly together with the heads upward, and spread two more for cap-sheaves, to form a sort of roof over the shock. Two men, working hard and steadily, could barely keep up with the binder.

After the wheat was in the shocks, where it would dry and cure for two or three weeks, the oats were harvested in the same way.

Then came time to thresh the wheat and oats. Jimmy enjoyed the excitement, as the slow-moving traction engine came puffing into the barnyard, hauling the "separator" behind it. While Spencer showed the engineer where he wanted the straw stacked, a half-dozen wagons and a dozen men arrived from neighboring farms. Threshing required so much labor that it was a coöperative job. Neighbors drove their wagons to the field. The bundle pitchers, usually two to the wagon, lifted the bundles with pitchforks to the wagon, where the driver arranged the load. If he were so careless that a part of it slipped off, he could expect to be laughed at for the rest of the day.

When the load reached the threshing place, the driver pitched his bundles, one by one, into the front of the separator. The twine bands, were slashed, and whirling, spiked cylinders beat the grain off the straw; fans blew out the chaff, and the grain poured into sacks at the side. The straw was blown from the rear of the machine into a stack.

Two men attended the sacks as they filled at the side of the dusty separator, tied them, and set them on a wagon. Filled with the customary two bushels, each sack of wheat weighed 120 pounds. It had to be lifted again from the wagon and emptied into a granary. Some months later, the grain would be reloaded and taken to market.

No sooner had the harvest ended than Spencer Logan set the hired man to plowing one of the grain fields. The wheat was to be sown in late September, but the sooner the field could be plowed, the better next year's yield would be.

This was the time, too, for a thorough cleaning of barns and stables; and a hundred loads or more of manure waited to be spread over the fields for fertilizer.

By the last week in August or the first week in September, the corn was ripe enough to cut. Armed with long, sharp knives, Spencer and the hired man slashed off the stalks about a foot from the ground, carried them, one armload at a time, to a shock which, when finished, was tied around the top with selected cornstalks. This went on for weeks. Jimmy helped until school opened. On the thirty acres of corn, more than 300,000 stalks had to be cut and carried.

After that terrific task was finished and the wheat was sown, corn-husking began. The shocked stalks were laid horizontally on the ground, the husks peeled back, and the ears broken off and thrown into a pile. Later, the piled ears were gathered in baskets, lifted into a wagon, and shoveled into a crib. From the crib, the corn was taken as needed during the year, a basketful at a time, and carried to feed the farm animals. From cutting to feeding, each ear of Spencer's corn was handled and carried five or six times. The stalks, after husking, were tied in bundles, and later brought to the barn for feed and bedding.

Spencer always expected to finish cornhusking by Thanksgiving Day. With hay mows, granaries, and cribs full, he was ready for winter. Then, from the Chicago stockyards, a carload of thin and hungry Western steers came to the barn. Morning and evening, seven days a week, their mangers were cleaned and filled. Cows were milked, horses and hogs fed. The steers grew fat and sleek and, before spring plowing time, were sold.

On winter days, trees were cut and, with ax and crosscut saw, made into logs and firewood. Drainage ditches were dug by lifting a spadeful of dirt at a time. After heavy tile had been hauled from town and placed end to end in the ditch bottoms, the excavated earth was pushed back in place. Postholes were dug and fences repaired. The morning and evening chores usually included carrying a dozen buckets of water to the animals. Milking was done by hand.

Spencer's muscles, and the hired man's, and Jimmy's were never soft, though they were often mighty tired.

Years afterward, when Jimmy was asked why he had not become a farmer, like his father, his reply reflected the feelings of many farm boys of his time. "I found out early," he said, "that nearly everything on the farm had to be picked up and that nearly everything was heavy!"

CHAPTER 7

Engines
Multiply Muscles

All the wealth people possess and enjoy is the product of energy intelligently applied to natural resources. Even a lazy tropical savage, lounging under a coconut tree, has to exert energy to pick up a coconut, if he wants to eat.

Farmers in America have steadily tried to find more productive ways of applying energy to the soil. When they had to rely largely upon their own muscles, they adopted the cradle, in place of the sickle, to harvest grain. With the same effort, they could accomplish more. Later, with the reaper and many other inventions, they literally harnessed the energy of horses and mules. Then, from steam, from internal-combustion engines, and from electricity came new sources of energy, which revolutionized the age-old art of farming. The farmer now had at his command the vastly stepped-up energy of "engine muscles."

A century and a quarter ago, a farmer who used a walking plow and a brush harrow, broadcast the seed by hand, cut his grain with a sickle or cradle, and threshed it with a flail could produce twenty bushels of wheat from an acre, by working from fifty to sixty hours.

His grandson, with the benefit of the horse-drawn machinery that was up to date in 1900 and the steam thresher could do the same work in eight hours.

Fifty years later, a great-great-grandson driving tractor machinery needed only three or four hours to raise his twenty bushels of wheat from one acre.

The man who had to work fifty hours to get his twenty bushels spent money only for his horse, plow, and cradle. He had probably saved his seed and whittled out his flail. Today, his great-great-grandson has to invest thousands of dollars in machinery—dollars that go to hire the energy of men who mine the iron, make the steel, shape the machines, and handle their transportation. Even so, the total procedure is ultimately more economical in terms of dollars and energy. Bread today would be costly indeed, if wheat were still produced by the methods of 1830.

The reaper, the steel plow, and the improved horse-drawn machinery applied the muscles of men and animals more efficiently. Each advance in mechanical equipment has aimed at economizing energy.

Imaginative farmers, who watched steamboats travel up the rivers, saw steam locomotives roaring along the railroad tracks, and gaped at stationary steam engines turning saw-and gristmills, naturally wondered about applying the great power which steam could generate to plowing their fields.

Many attempts to use steam power were made. Ideas for steam plows were in the air as early as 1830; and by 1877, some ninety American and British inventions in this field had been listed in the patent offices. The inventors could not always raise the money to make even sample machines. The first machines appear to have been based on the principle of a stationary engine which wound cables around a drum and drew a plow across a field. Later, moving engines were built which agitated the soil with teeth or blades. These "land locomotives," as some called them, cost from three to ten thousand dollars, too expensive for any but the largest farms and actually too costly for any farm, because they failed to work well. Finally, late in the nineteenth century, traction engines were developed, which could move themselves and also pull a

McManigal

As late as the 1930's, steam power, with its obvious fire hazard, was used to operate threshing machines. Here, men pitch bundles from the grain stacks to the separator. Straw stack appears at extreme right in front of windmill.

load. They were equipped with steel gears, suitable driving wheels, and carried water and fuel. Some were built with 120 horsepower, able to pull twenty or thirty plows at a time. Such monsters began service on the level land of big wheat farms in the American and Canadian prairie country, but were soon replaced by a more economical and efficient type of engine.

Steampower was produced by heat, from fuel burned outside the engine cylinder. During the latter half of the nineteenth century, several European inventors found ways to make engines whose fuel could be burned inside the cylinder. Gasoline, mixed with air, was exploded with regularity in controlled quantities.

These internal-combustion engines, useful for many purposes, made the automobile possible.

When the automobile began to displace the buggy and the driving horse, the motorization of agriculture had its real beginnings. Though the buggy was not a field tool, it became indispensable to farmers. With their homes on land which might be two, ten, or even more miles from a trading center, road transportation was essential to transaction of their business, obtaining of supplies, and leading a social life. The first automobiles were too expensive for most farm families, although the more prosperous farmers did not wait long to buy them. Then, in 1908, Henry Ford began to manufacture his low-price Model T, the car that put America on the road. By 1920, more than two million farmers owned cars.

Impressed by the advantages of speed and power, and by the distances their automobiles could cover economically, farmers became more eager than ever for a mechanical horse to do their field work. Through their cars, they grew familiar with the workings of the internal-combustion engine, and thus were prepared for the motorized tractor.

Meanwhile, the engine that burned its fuel inside was learning to plow. Gasoline tractors made their first appearance about 1905 and, on some of the big farms, the huge, open-geared machines supplanted the steam outfits. Shortly after World War I, smaller and safer tractors with enclosed gears appeared. Except for farms of one thousand acres or more, the tractor had not yet become a practical source of power. Even so, nearly a quarter-million of the machines were in use by 1920.

The average-sized farm could not afford a tractor until 1930 or later, mainly because it was too expensive for the number of jobs it could do. Farmers still had to maintain at least one team of horses; in fact, a horseless farm was unheard of until late in the 1920's. Now, in the 1960's, there are more farm tractors than farms.

The earlier tractors were designed as substitutes for horses.

Farmers hitched their horse-drawn types of implements behind them. Enginepower, they found, could pull much bigger loads, so they devised ways to hitch on still more equipment. Because the tractor could move faster than a team of horses, it soon became apparent that stronger implements were needed, designed to take full advantage of the new power and speed. As the tractor itself evolved still further, the machinery it operated continued to change. Since the tractor could push and carry as well as pull, cultivators and other machines were invented to attach to the front of the engine, where the operator could watch the work from the seat. Rubber tires appeared in the mid-thirties, adding yet more speed, power, and economy to tractor operations.

As the tractor evolved to a point where it could do not only any work horses could do, but other kinds of jobs as well, farmers envisioned hundreds of things which could be accomplished quickly by some form of enginepower, if suitable equipment could be devised. Along with experiment-station engineers and manufacturers' designers, farmers worked out machines to pick cotton, gather fruit, feed chickens, and to perform a multitude of tasks which had always been done by hand.

While the tractor was being adapted to constantly greater versatility, another form of enginepower was becoming available to farmers. This was electricity. Farmers had long looked enviously at the electric lights in the homes and stores of their town friends, and had often seen electric motors at work. The electric-power companies seldom extended their lines far beyond the towns; since the rural areas were so sparsely settled, they felt that it would not be profitable.

Two developments brought about a rapid change in this situation. One was the development of new appliances, that used electric motors and current to do many more kinds of work in the farm home and outbuildings. The other was the authorization, in 1936, by Congress of the Rural Electrification Administration, an agency which was authorized to lend money to coöperative farm groups and others planning to build and operate electric lines. The existence of this agency stimulated the private companies to greater efforts.

Today, nine out of ten farms are electrified; and the average current consumption is much greater than in city homes, because of the many jobs electricity performs. Farm homes are equipped with food freezers, refrigerators, electric stoves, dishwashers, laundry machines, water heaters, vacuum cleaners, toasters, and television. In addition, electricity has taken over countless outside chores that once consumed endless hours of time and energy.

Thus, with the internal-combustion engine and electric current at their command, farmers have made seven-league strides— and have far fewer backaches. The remark has often been made that a farmer from the Nile Valley of a pharaoh's day could have handled, without instruction, almost any equipment or task he might have found on an American farm in George Washington's time. Now it can be said that a man who quit farming in 1920 would be lost on a present-day farm, and even one who quit in 1950 would have much to learn.

Today, the most efficient farmers grow a bushel of corn with

The corn combine not only husks two rows at a time, but also shells the corn. Some models include a drier, which reduces the moisture content of the corn.

U.S.D.A. photo

five minutes of labor, as compared with seventy-two minutes in the years before power machinery was used. The tractor handles equipment which sprays the fields to prevent weeds or destroy insects, spreads fertilizers with precision, and, at harvest, rapidly picks the ears of corn and hauls them to the cribs, where an electric motor lifts them into storage. Machines will also dry the corn if necessary, and shell the grains from the cobs.

Making hay has become a fast-moving, one-man task. In one system, the tractor draws a machine which picks up the hay, crushes and ties it into bales, and tosses the bales into a wagon hitched behind the baler. Elevators and conveyors store the hay in the barn. In another system, the hay is chopped into short lengths as it is picked up, blown into self-unloading wagons, and then into the barn. Artificial drying methods are also used.

Tractor-drawn drills efficiently sow wheat and other small grains. Harvesting moves swiftly, as the tractors draw machines which cut and thresh the grain in a single operation, and pour it into wagons or trucks. On the Great Plains wheat fields, self-propelled combine harvesters can thresh 1,500 bushels a day.

Ingenious machines now pick cotton two rows at a time, doing as much as eighty hand pickers. Flame-throwers burn weeds from four rows of cotton at once.

Nowadays, forward-looking farmers store feed so that, by the push of a button, it moves automatically to the trough. It may even be separated, weighed out, and mixed to fit the needs of individual animals. Automatic barn-cleaners remove manure, and either deliver it directly to a spreader or stack it, so that with a fork-lift on a tractor the farmer can load and unload it in a few minutes.

In dairy barns, electrically operated milking machines pipe milk directly into bulk cooling tanks, so that it is never exposed to air. Tank trucks pump it out and carry it to processing plants. One man can take care of fifty cows, and if they are highly productive, well-fed animals, he may produce 500,000 pounds of milk a year, enough to supply nearly 1,400 people.

In the poultry business, one man can feed, water, and gather eggs from 10,000 hens. He can care for 25,000 broilers at a time. Since broilers are sold at the age of three months, he can raise 100,000 of them in a year.

As a result of the new machinery operated by electric and gasoline power, plus many scientific advances, the output for a farm worker is eighty per cent greater than in 1940. The investment in land and equipment for a typical mechanized farm runs to more than fifty thousand dollars. Only men who are able and versatile can be successful in modern agriculture. This is a vast change from earlier times, when a farmer was said to need "only a weak mind and a strong back."

An auger in the loaded trailer pours a feed mixture into the cattle bunks on a Maryland farm.

U.S.D.A. photo

CHAPTER 8

From Everywhere
to Everywhere

Until the nineteenth century was well advanced, every farmer's first aim was to produce food for his own family. Then, if he could raise more than was needed at home, he looked for a place to sell or trade his surplus.

Corn and wheat went to the gristmill to be ground. Cows were kept for milk and butter, and poultry for eggs and meat. Hams and bacon were hung in the smokehouse, a steer was fattened to butcher in early winter, and potatoes and turnips were stored in the cellar. The women of the farm dried corn and apples and, after the process of canning was understood, they stored fruit and vegetables in cans.

Though the farmer handled little cash all year, his family usually enjoyed an abundance of food. People in the villages and small towns, too, often kept a cow and some chickens, and cultivated a garden patch.

In the colonial and pioneer years, farm people made most of their own clothing. The women spun and wove their home-grown flax, wool, or cotton. Hides were saved until an itinerant cobbler came along, to make boots and shoes.

However, there were always unsatisfied wants. The farm did not produce salt, spices, or coffee, nor powder and lead for ammunition. The cobbler might accept a sheep for his shoemaking and a calf might be bartered for a new table, but the farmer wanted also to sell for ready cash. He might have several surplus sheep or calves, and, in a good year, several bushels of wheat to spare; so he looked for markets. As the clearings grew wider and as the pioneers pushed farther westward, this need for markets became ever more pressing; cash markets, if possible.

With nine-tenths of the people still engaged in farming in 1790, the other tenth offered no great market. Farmers who lived near the towns peddled a few fruits and vegetables from door to door and sold fresh meat when the fall butchering time came. In the larger towns, a dairyman hauled milk along the streets, and ladled it into containers which the housewives brought to his cart.

Soon, however, the farms out in the Ohio Valley had wheat and corn, wool and salt pork well beyond their needs. Rivers provided the cheapest transportation, but nature hadn't designed rivers to run over the mountains. So the Ohio Valley people began floating their produce downstream to New Orleans, a city which the French owned.

Then, in 1802, President Jefferson wrote:

There is on the globe one single spot, the possessor of which is our natural and habitual enemy. It is New Orleans, through which the produce of three-eighths of our territory must pass to market and from its fertility it will ere long yield more than half of our whole produce, and contain more than half of our inhabitants.

So Jefferson bought Louisiana, and in doing so changed the history of North America.

New routes to markets, markets that would return cash to farmers, were in the minds of many men. By 1805, an idea developed that did not depend on rivers. Cattle and hogs could walk to market, even though the distance was several hundred miles. Men bought livestock from Ohio and Kentucky farmers, and patiently drove the animals eastward to Baltimore and Philadelphia. About 1818, Cincinnatians began packing pork in barrels of brine, for shipment to New Orleans or wherever buyers could be found. Cincinnati became known as "Porkopolis."

Men, who appreciated the great advantages of waterways for transportation, talked of building canals even before the Revolutionary War. George Washington, in 1785, headed a company that planned a canal to connect the Potomac and Ohio rivers; it was only partly finished fifty years after Washington's death and was never successful.

In 1825, New York State completed the famous Erie Canal, which reached 363 miles from Buffalo, on Lake Erie, to Troy, on the Hudson River. "DeWitt Clinton's Ditch," it was called by skeptics who ridiculed the builder and his ideas. They were wrong, for the canal soon paid for the enormous labor expended during the more than eight years of digging. Grain and produce started to move from the Western farm country to the Atlantic. Manufactured goods could now be shipped westward at low cost; and emigrants, with their goods, could travel west by canal boat, a great improvement over the wagon. No longer did the long Appalachian range present a costly barrier to trade between the populous East and the lands of opportunity in the Mississippi Valley and around the Great Lakes.

The booming success of the Erie Canal inspired Ohio to dig a canal on each side of the state between Lake Erie and the Ohio River. Indiana and Ohio built one up the Maumee River from Lake Erie and down the Wabash River which reached the Ohio near Evansville, Indiana. The 452-mile distance made this the longest American canal.

The appearance of the "Iron Horse," the locomotive, put an end to the building of canals. Railroads, a faster and cheaper way of transportation, soon spread across America. Beginning in 1829 with short routes, the rails reached Chicago in 1852, the Mississippi two years later, Council Bluffs on the Missouri in 1866. Then, in 1869, the golden spike was driven near Ogden, Utah, to dramatize the completion of the first transcontinental track. Rail-

ways and farmers made history together. The produce and purchases of farmers provided cargo for the railroads; the lengthening
rail lines assured markets for the ever-advancing settlers. Refrig-
erated cars, which appeared in 1870, permitted slaughtering of
livestock closer to the farms, and shipment of perishable fruits
and vegetables over long distances.

Railway owners, well aware that their roads were the sole
means by which farmers could reach distant city markets, yielded
to the temptation to set their rates high. The farmers retaliated.
Gaining political power by organizing themselves, they forced rate
regulations through state legislatures and, in 1887, obtained federal laws that provided controls by the Interstate Commerce
Commission.

After World War I, the motor truck began hauling grain and
livestock to the railroad points. As better highways were built, the
trucks served farmers over longer and longer distances, moving
cattle and hogs direct from farms to the packing houses, carrying

This big truck transports a double-deck load of hogs to market.

U.S.D.A. photo

milk from Wisconsin to Florida, oranges from Florida to Illinois.
Together, the motor truck, highway, and railroad made it possible
for farmers everywhere to find markets for their products, all within a century from the time when the canal towboat was the fastest
and cheapest method of transport.

During this hundred years, cities and towns grew prodigiously.
The urban populations, employed in industry and commerce, paid
less attention to gardens or had no room for them. Sanitary regulations forbade keeping pigs, cows, or chickens in populated
areas. The neighborhood and downtown stores became the sources
of food, and to supply the stores, larger wholesale establishments
became essential.

These changes opened the way for "middlemen." Their
work varied to fit the needs of each commodity and each part of
the nation. The Western ranchman could consign cattle in carload
lots to the Chicago stockyards, where commission firms found
buyers, either among the meat packers or among farmers. In other
areas, country livestock buyers went from farm to farm, looking
for small lots or even single animals which they assembled in carloads for shipment to market terminals. More and more, farming
and merchandising became separate though related enterprises.

Wherever grains were produced in quantity, tall storage elevators were built on railroad sidings. Usually, the elevator owner
bought from the farmer and sold to a larger firm, which in turn
supplied the millers and other grain processors. Packaged flour,
breakfast foods, and other consumer products were then distributed by wholesalers and jobbers to the retail grocers.

After World War II, the supermarket appeared, replacing the
neighborhood grocery store, butcher shop, and fruit stand, which
for decades had served local consumers. Formerly, the small-town
butcher had purchased animals from nearby farmers and prepared
the meat cuts himself; the city butcher bought sides of beef and
cleaned carcasses of hogs or lambs, which he cut up to suit
his customers. The larger cities maintained wholesale market sec-

At some sixty terminal markets livestock can be bought and sold on any business day. Chicago and Omaha are the largest markets.

tions, where the retailers came to buy meats and perishable fruits and vegetables. Semiperishable items, such as potatoes and apples, were stored on farms after the harvests, to be shipped later to the cities. Until transportation became swift and safe, consumers were lucky if they could buy fresh green vegetables at any time other than the growing season.

Half a century has elapsed since the local food merchant weighed crackers and sugar out of barrels, prunes out of bulk boxes, and sold potatoes by the peck. Today, we take for granted the sanitary "packaging" of an amazing range of foods in cardboard, cellophane, and polyethylene containers.

And frozen foods—another amazing development—how did they come about? The process was discovered in the 1930's by an observant New England man, Clarence Birdseye. While he was fishing through the ice in Labrador in twenty below zero weather, he observed that the fish he caught froze almost instantly. Due to this quick freezing, he noted, the ice crystals in their bodies were so small they did not break up the flesh when the fish thawed. He then experimented and discovered that the idea could be applied to other foods, as well as fish. As a result, within twenty years frozen food cabinets became familiar fixtures in stores throughout America, stocked with fish, meats, fruits, vegetables, juices, and even complete meals.

Now let's take a look at the complex system of modern-day food distribution. As an example of how it works, and what it costs, we'll follow the trip of a pig from an Iowa farm to a New York consumer.

Dean Wolf, a *Farm Journal* reporter, traveled with the hogs to get the story. One morning a truck picked up thirty-one hogs from a farm in eastern Iowa. The trucker took them to a nearby town, reloaded them into a semitrailer, and headed for Chicago. So far costs were 63½ cents for each 100 pounds, 50 cents for the truck, 12 cents for insurance, and a 3 per cent federal tax on the trucking charge.

The stockyards in Chicago charged $11.16 for keeping the hogs overnight and $4.20 for two bushels of corn to feed them. Fire insurance cost 7 cents, and 21 cents went to the National Livestock and Meat Board, an organization which promotes the eating of meat and which, of course, the livestock industry supports.

Then a commission firm sold the hogs to a packing company for $14.00 a hundredweight and charged $11.78, or 38 cents a hog, for making the deal. After all the charges up to this point had been deducted, the Iowa farmer received $12.88 per hundred-weight, not quite 13 cents a pound.

The packer, knowing that Easterners will pay more for fresh-killed pork than for meat shipped from the Midwest, decided to send the thirty-one live hogs to his processing plant in Jersey City. The hogs had now cost the packer $16.48 per hundred pounds, and, unhappily, had lost twelve pounds each on the trip.

When the packer had slaughtered the hogs and cut up the meat, what did he have to sell? His figures showed 25 pounds of ham, $8.64; 12 pounds of picnics, $2.53; 20½ pounds of belly, $5.00; 20 pounds of loin, $6.54; 3 pounds of spare ribs, 87 cents; 2 pounds of neck bones, 11 cents; 3½ pounds of feet, 20 cents; ¼ pound of tail, 1 cent; 4½ pounds of skinned jowls, 50 cents; 4¼ pounds of trimmings, 76 cents; 7 pounds of "variety meats" (brains, tongue, liver, etc.), 94 cents; 27½ pounds of lard, $2.92; by-products, 66 cents.

These meats went in different directions. Reporter Wolf followed the twenty pounds of pork loin, which were sent to a large chain grocery in New York. There, he saw the loin sliced, the chops wrapped in cellophane packages and priced at 79 cents a pound. A woman came along and looked over the assorted meats on display, finally deciding on the fresh center-cut chops from the hogs that had left Iowa just a week before. When she learned that Mr. Wolf had been following her chops all the way from Iowa to this meat counter, she bought two more and invited him to have dinner with the family.

Thus, in the 79 cent-a-pound pork chops was pay for the Iowa farmer for his corn and labor; the Iowa trucker, the Detroit workers who made the truck, and the Akron men who made its tires; the people in Chicago, Jersey City, New York, and others along the line. Nor is that all. The farmer, the truckmen, the railroad, and everybody concerned had to pay taxes.

It has often been repeated that no one enjoys more independence than the farmer who works on his own land in his own way.

Independent he is in many ways, but he does have one boss: the consumer. The lady who bought the pork chops might, for many reasons, have decided to buy beef from some other Iowa farm, chicken from Georgia, turkey from Virginia, lamb from Colorado, or fish from Maine. Instead of meat, she could have spent her money for oranges from Florida, lettuce from California, rice from Arkansas, sugar from Louisiana, apples from New York, potatoes from Idaho, spinach from Texas, eggs from Missouri, frozen berries from Washington, pears from Oregon, dried peas from Utah, beans from Michigan—literally something from every corner of the nation and many items from abroad. Farmers and the market system provide the shopper with many choices. What she and her family like and can afford determines what the store will stock; and that, in turn, decides what farmers will plant.

An intricate, nationwide system of market reporting reaches from the consuming centers to the producing areas. Farmers watch their newspapers, listen to radio reports, and study the market trends daily. Fresh, perishable produce, which must be sold quickly, presents a different problem from that of grain, which can be stored for months, and yet again different from livestock.

The distribution system has developed, as men have seen opportunities to make their living by providing services that people are willing to buy. Free competition has created it; government could not have designed it, and has intervened only to prevent unscrupulous or greedy men from taking unfair advantages. Consumers may choose from a tremendous variety of foodstuffs, and independent farmers can always find a market.

CHAPTER 9

The South
Forges Ahead

In the Southern parts of the United States agriculture has developed differently than in the North and West. Climate, soils, distance from markets, and historic circumstances are the reasons.

Climate gave the South a near monopoly of cotton, rice, sugar, and tobacco. Until recent times, each of these crops depended on human labor, giving rise to the slavery which for many years characterized Southern agriculture.

Negro slavery, first brought to Virginia in 1619, was extended throughout the colonies during the eighteenth century. Of some half-million slaves in 1776, nearly fifty thousand were owned in the Middle colonies and New England. Economic and moral considerations put an end to slave-holding in most of these states soon after the Revolution began, although, under gradual emancipation laws, slavery was permitted in New York until 1827 and in New Jersey until 1846. Northern agriculture couldn't make use of slave labor profitably; the variety of crops demanded a variety of skills. Neither did slave labor prove productive in industrial ventures.

On the other hand, the monotonous, repetitive tasks of cotton and rice farming, the heavy hand labor of sugar cane production, and the toilsome routines of the tobacco fields could be performed readily by slaves. The Negroes could have learned skills and taken

71

on responsibilities, but as slaves they had no incentive. Under overseers, they were kept at simple tasks, such as hoeing cotton; even the slave women and children earned their support by doing field work.

Except to the tobacco planters, farming brought little prosperity to the South until the mid-eighteenth century. Credit goes to a little English girl named Eliza Lucas, for establishing one of the first profitable crops. This was indigo, a plant which produced a valuable cloth dye. Eliza's father, a British officer who was lieutenant governor of Antigua in the West Indies, inherited three plantations near Charleston. When he came to visit them, in 1738, he brought Eliza along. Though she was only sixteen, he left her in charge of twenty slaves and the mortgaged plantations. Of the crops she experimented with, indigo proved most promising. She learned to grow the plant and to prepare the dye for market, and her knowledge was passed on to others. In 1748, the British government began paying sixpence a pound bounty on indigo shipped to England, and in one year alone a million pounds were exported. For about thirty years, the crop was produced in considerable quantity. Then, because the bounty was withdrawn, indigo production declined and eventually stopped.

It would make a better story if we could report that Eliza's indigo crops paid off the mortgages, but the plantations were lost. Nevertheless, Eliza herself came through well. She married an important South Carolinian, and became the mother of two sons, who gave distinguished service to their country as Revolutionary soldiers and statesmen. They were Charles Cotesworth Pinckney and Thomas Pinckney; among other honors, both were strongly supported for the presidency and vice-presidency.

Even before the introduction of indigo to the South, farmers began to grow rice along the coast of South Carolina. The grain flourished, and the few hundred planters there and in Georgia who owned suitable land soon became rich. They built lavish plantation estates, owned stately homes in Charleston and Savannah, and sent their sons to England to be educated. Most rice is grown where the fields can be flooded, particularly on the flat lands near the ocean, where waters flowing from higher country can be held as needed. After 1783, a system of banks, sluices, and ditches utilized the fresh-water tides, and rice planting continued to prosper in South Carolina until the Civil War. Eventually, low prices, unfavorable weather, and competition from further west caused failures, and the coastal marshes returned to their primitive condition. Low-lying areas in Louisiana, Arkansas, and Texas then became the primary sources of rice, because the machinery which had been developed could be used more effectively there. These states and the lower Sacramento Valley in California are still the leading rice producers. Today, rice is sown by airplanes and harvested by com-bines, and American growers can undersell the Chinese and Japanese in their own markets.

Although cotton was grown in small quantities almost from the time of the earliest Southern settlements, it did not become important until after the Revolution. At that time, power-operated textile machinery appeared in England. In order to hold a monop-oly on the machinery, England forbade its export, prohibited the sending of information about its construction out of the country, and barred any textile worker from emigrating. But these laws were not enough to stop a young fellow named Samuel Slater. He worked around the new machinery until he knew all about it, then, just twenty-one, he evaded the officials, and set out for America. From memory he designed, and with local financial support built, a cotton mill at Pawtucket, Rhode Island, in 1793 and so put the new country into the cotton-manufacturing business.

Slater arrived in 1789; Whitney invented the cotton gin in 1793. These enterprising young men were to see a great manufac-turing industry develop in the Northeast and a vast cotton-growing empire spread across the South. Much of the nation's history for the next hundred years was to be influenced by their achievements.

With good prices for cotton in both domestic and foreign

markets, crop acreage expanded rapidly. Planters opened up virgin lands in Alabama, Mississippi, and Texas, and these new states grew steadily.

Cotton and slavery led the South to oppose the tariffs, which were designed to encourage manufacturing in the North. The desire to acquire new cotton lands and to spread slavery were factors in the annexation of Texas and the consequent war with Mexico. They became heated issues upon the admission of new states—which were to be slave and which free? Despite compromises in 1820 and 1850, the extremists, North and South, whipped up such violent feelings that the tragic Civil War eventually erupted. The war ended slavery and left the South in ruins and poverty.

In 1860, the slave states had a white population of about 8,000,000. Of these, 383,000 were slaveowners. Less than one-third of the owners had more than 10 slaves; only 2,292 owned 100 or more. It is interesting to note that the Constitution of the Confederate States prohibited the further importation of slaves.

After the Civil War ended, a new system placed cotton growing largely in the hands of tenants and sharecroppers. To adjust to new ways and to build new capital took many years, but by 1880, cotton again became the country's foremost export. Then, for nearly half a century planters from South Carolina to Texas paid little attention to any other crop. The Negro tenants and sharecroppers plowed the fields, planted, chopped, hoed, and picked the cotton. An acre that yielded one five hundred-pound bale was considered remarkable; the South's average cotton acre produced a hundred and fifty to two hundred pounds.

Big changes in Southern agriculture began to occur after World War I. First, tractors took over the job of plowing, then of cultivation. Many Negroes, deprived of their accustomed full season's field work, began trekking North to find jobs, while small farmers in South Carolina and Georgia found it hard to compete with the large operations on the western Texas plains. California, especially the southern part of the San Joaquin Valley, had also moved into cotton.

By the end of World War II, the mechanical cotton picker had been greatly improved. Airplanes spread insect sprays and dusts with swift efficiency. New weed killers destroyed weeds without damaging cotton, and government restrictions upon crop acreage led to the use of more powerful fertilizers. The 1920 harvest was thirteen million bales from thirty-six million acres, while the 1955 harvest was fourteen million bales from seventeen million acres. The old days of the small cotton patch had vanished into the dim past.

Though the cotton-growing center has shifted westward and the methods have changed, cotton remains a major crop in the Carolinas and Georgia. It is still produced in the border states and even in southern Illinois. But the old South is no longer a one-crop area—a crop that for so many decades produced poverty for

A fleet of mechanical cotton pickers moving through a field on a large Mississippi plantation.

U.S.D.A. photo

the many and wealth for only a few. Nutritious varieties of Southern grasses have stimulated the pasturing and feeding of livestock, especially cattle. Improved strains of hybrid corn, bred to fit the warmer climate, have enabled farmers to produce more feed for livestock. Professional corn growers in the corn belt states were astonished, in 1955, to learn that a Mississippi boy, a 4-H club member, had a world record yield of 304 bushels on an acre, nearly 50 bushels above previous records. Improved refrigeration and quick-freezing have increased opportunities for poultry production. Rising demands locally and in the North turned many Southern farms to vegetable crops, sold fresh, frozen, or canned.

The paper-making industries learned to utilize the pines which grew on the coastal plains, built mills to manufacture kraft papers, newsprint, and pulp for rayon. Their mills provided new jobs, and markets for farmers who own woodlands.

Other industries, attracted by the mild climate, reliable labor supply, and growing prosperity, have erected factories in Southern towns and cities. And thousands of small farmers have found that by using power machinery they can take advantage of industrial job opportunities, working forty hours a week in a factory, and still raise their crops at home.

The present agriculture of the South contrasts sharply with that of pre-Civil War days and with that of the long dismal decades of the Reconstruction. The change has been dramatic, more so than the changes in the North, because it came even more quickly. With a climate that provides a long growing season and with a wide diversity of soils, the future looks bright for the farmers of the South.

CHAPTER 10

The Enemies
of Harvest

Imagine a midsummer cloud half a mile high, a hundred miles wide, and three hundred miles long—a cloud not of raindrops but grasshoppers! This torrent of insects, darkening the sun, falls upon trees, grass, crops, devouring every green blade, leaf, and stalk. Behind them, fields are left utterly barren. Only holes in the earth remain to show where green plants were growing a few short hours before.

That, in actual fact, describes what happened in Nebraska and Kansas in 1873–1874, to farmers who suffered almost unbelievably destructive invasions by these winged insects. They had come before, in 1864 and 1866, and were to appear again later. In 1923, grasshoppers destroyed all the crops in Montana.

Farmers wage an unceasing war against insects that destroy crops, weaken and kill livestock, and spread diseases among plants and animals. Sometimes the insects win a total victory and the farmers go bankrupt, as they did in the grasshopper invasions and again when the boll weevil first attacked the cotton in Texas. Every year, insects in some way or another gain a partial victory over the farmers. Counting the crops and property they destroy, and the poisons and time spent in fighting them, insects cost us the huge sum of four billion dollars a year.

The colonists, who began farming their cleared tracts in the

Eastern forests, were on the lookout for bears and wolves. They probably paid little attention to the damage done by less conspicuous enemies. The virgin soil had not yet been contaminated by the debris of repeated crops, in which insects lay eggs and find shelter. The balance of nature had not yet been upset.

In an absolute wilderness, each kind of animal, bird, and insect finds its food. Each species feeds on some other species, but none becomes overabundant and none is likely to be crowded out. Farming changes all this. Instead of a land covered with varieties of trees and wild plants, many acres are devoted to a single crop. The insect that once fed on certain wild plants growing here and there, suddenly finds new plants, equally suited to its taste, concentrated in big fields. Within a short time, because of the great increase in its food supply, the insect multiplies enormously and becomes a dreaded pest.

Until 1859, farmers knew nothing about the Colorado potato beetle. This striped insect, less than a half-inch long, lived near the Rocky Mountains and ate wild plants of the Solanum genus (or type). Farmers came to nearby Nebraska and planted potatoes, which also belong to the Solanum genus. The beetles promptly moved to the lush new pastures. Producing two or three new generations a season and able to fly, beetles reached Ohio ten years later and, by 1874, had spread to the Atlantic coast—fifteen hundred miles in fifteen years. Millions of farm boys and girls spent wearying hours with a short stick and a bucket, collecting the potato beetles that were later drowned in kerosene. Now, machines spread sprays and dusts, which keep these enemies under control.

As damage to their crops increased, farmers turned to science for help. But entomology—the study of insects—was just developing in those days. A professor of natural history at Harvard University, William D. Peck, had made a beginning when, in 1795, he published a paper on cankerworms, a destroyer of fruit and shade trees. The United States Patent Office (which came before the Department of Agriculture) and the State of New York, both in 1854, employed entomologists. A dozen years later, Illinois and Missouri also hired these scientists. After the state Experiment Stations were established, beginning in 1888, more scientists set to work to find methods for checking insect ravages. Today, more than two hundred field offices and laboratories conduct research, study control measures, and advise farmers how to keep ahead of the bugs. In addition, insecticide manufacturers employ hundreds of scientists, who work to make their products more effective against insects, as well as safe for people to handle.

The 1952 United States Department of Agriculture *Yearbook* claims that North America is home to 82,500 species of insects, and 2,613 kinds of ticks and mites (technically not insects, though related). Ten thousand of these may be considered public enemies, though the F.B.I. can't get at them, unfortunately. Some six hundred kinds are harmful enough to be of prime importance. A majority of the worst pests are not natives; they came to America with the people or hitchhiked on imported goods.

A man who was a great scientist and who devoted most of his long life—ninety-three years—to enlisting Americans in the war against insects was Leland Ossian Howard. He was born in Illinois

This 1891 photo shows Dr. L.O. Howard (*standing, center*) in the Office of Entomology, United States Department of Agriculture.

U.S.D.A. photo

in 1857. At the age of twenty-one, he became one of the first three entomologists in the Department of Agriculture, and for a third of a century he was chief of the Bureau of Entomology. "Is man or insect better qualified to inhabit this globe?" he asked. "Every year the damage wrought by insects nullifies the labor of a million men." Howard named the common housefly "the typhoid fly," because it carried typhoid-fever germs. He stirred up nationwide "Swat-the-Fly!" campaigns, to reduce the numbers of disease-spreading flies. His scientific work opened the way for controlling yellow fever and malaria. On trip after trip to Europe, he tracked down different types of insects which would destroy the harmful imported species already thriving in the United States. In more than a thousand articles and pamphlets, he reported his scientific findings, arousing people to action against the insect menace. He also persuaded Congress to finance his bureau in extending its studies and publicizing its findings.

Associated with Howard, and later to become his successor, was Charles L. Marlatt. Knowing the trouble that farmers had suffered from imported insects, Marlatt was determined to find a way to prevent other destructive visitors from getting a foothold. His plan, finally accepted by Congress, was for a plant quarantine operation. Now, as a result, no plant may come from abroad without undergoing a stay in "quarantine," where it is thoroughly inspected by men who know how to look for insects, their larvae, and eggs.

When King George III sent his hired Hessians to America in 1776, he expected them to help quash the Revolution. They didn't manage to do that, but with them came a formidable enemy, whose damage even yet is calculated at sixteen million dollars a year. Hidden within the straw of the Hessians' bedding were the eggs and young of a tiny gnat. These creatures, living inside the wheat-stalk, cause straw to break down and prevent the grain from filling out. A particularly bad outbreak, in 1915, caused one hundred million dollars damage. Farmers now combat the Hessian fly by

Government inspectors examine plants entering the country at border stations and airports. Every effort is made to avoid introducing diseases or undesirable insects. Imported plants are detained at quarantine stations until free of danger, or fumigated in gas chambers.

delaying planting in the fall until after a "fly-free date," determined by the expected first frosts for each area. This way, the autumn brood of flies is unable to find young wheat in which to lay eggs, and their natural cycle is interrupted. Some fly-resistant varieties of wheat also have been developed.

No one knows how the European corn borer arrived in this country. The first of the pests was identified in Massachusetts in 1917. Relentlessly, at a rate of twenty to thirty miles a year, it spread westward. Efforts of the federal government—to the tune of ten million dollars in a single year—failed to stop it. Quarantine lines were established on westbound highways, to inspect all vehicles that might carry infested corn. Yet, in 1949, its most triumphant year, the borer cost corn producers $350 millions. The insect does most of its damage after the eggs hatch at the bottom of the cornstalk; then the larvae eat their way up inside the plant. Over two hundred borers per plant were counted in one Iowa county. Corn farmers destroy or plow under their old infested cornstalks and, where practicable, other plants nearby in which borers may hide. There are now varieties of corn which resist the borers' attack. Entomologists have brought from Europe a number of insects which are parasites of the corn borer, and these help to keep the number of corn borers down. Even so, thousands of farmers double their defense by spraying their corn fields with insecticides such as D.D.T.

Except for houseflies and mosquitoes, probably no insect is more familiar to Eastern Americans than the handsome Japanese beetle. With a hearty appetite for hundreds of plants, from weeds to roses, it probably originally slipped through quarantine in nursery stock. It was first seen near Riverton, New Jersey, in 1916. For years, no weapon proved effective against it. Finally, about 1940, scientists found "milky disease." Spores of this disease mixed with talc, can be dusted over the ground, where they infect the beetle grubs and kill most of them.

To the boll weevil, however, goes the prize for making more agricultural history than any other insect. This little creature, with a long snout, has bankrupted farmers and merchants, and has pried more money out of the federal treasury than any other six-legged animal. Since he first crossed the Rio Grande, about 1893, he has cost ten billion dollars in damaged cotton crops, still manages to destroy about fifteen per cent of the crop each year, yet has contributed importantly to increasing the yield per acre. He is really a "big shot" in the insect war against mankind.

By his tenth year as an undesirable alien, the boll weevil was creating havoc and panic. In two Texas counties, nearly half of the farmers abandoned their land and a third of the stores had to quit business. In that same year, 1903, the weevil reached Louisiana, and kept moving, 30 to 160 miles a year, until he came to the boundary of the cotton belt in Virginia. He stopped there, because he had an appetite only for cotton.

Meanwhile, the entomologists had been studying the habits of the detestable weevil. "Plow out and burn your old cottonstalks as early as you can, in the fall after picking," they told farmers. "Then, as early as you can in the spring, plant an early maturing variety. Fertilize it heavily. Your crop will get started well ahead of the weevil, and in spite of him you will get a good yield."

This advice sounded almost too simple to many farmers. They had long been advised by experts that these were good cotton-growing practices, weevil or no weevil, but few had paid much attention. To help overcome the lack of interest, the government actually paid some farmers to follow its advice. Their crops were good, but people then said anybody could do well with the government behind them. Finally, the dynamic Dr. Seaman A. Knapp appeared on the Texas scene as a special agent of the Department of Agriculture.

Knapp was born in northeastern New York. He had taught school in Vermont, raised livestock in Iowa, been president of Iowa State College, and grown rice in Louisiana. Seventy years old, he was full of energy. He knew human nature—that was his greatest asset—and he had an idea. He set out to find a leading farmer in each county, who would follow the recommended methods and who would then persuade a few other farmers to follow his example. The scheme worked. Knapp's idea eventually led to the creation of a nationwide organization of county-farm demonstration agents—a story to be told more fully in another chapter. Because farmers so greatly improved their work and began growing other crops and raising livestock in addition to cotton, a Chamber of Commerce in Alabama erected a monument to the boll weevil, the cause of it all.

The Mediterranean fruit fly—the only crop-destroying insect to have been completely eradicated—was first discovered in April,

1929, near Orlando, Florida. This creature punctures the skin of fruit and lays eggs inside, where the maggots feed, making the fruit inedible. Recognizing this pest as a threat to both citrus and deciduous fruits, the federal and state authorities went gunning for it in an all-out war. At a cost of more than seven million dollars, the Medfly, as it came to be called, was wiped out. For a quarter of a century, not one was seen until another infestation appeared in 1956. This time, again, it was eradicated.

The grasshopper, the potato beetle, and the Hessian fly, the corn borer, the Japanese beetle, the boll weevil, and the Medfly are only a few examples of the insects which battle with the farmers and with all of us for use of the earth. Nor have we heard about all the ways farmers are fighting back.

One of their weapons, chemical insecticides, can, in some instances, leave residues harmful to human health. So, scientists seek other methods that defeat the pests, and hunt for more living insect enemies. What happened to the screw-worm fly, which damaged livestock in Florida and nearby states, illustrates one new method of attack. By raising and sterilizing millions of male flies in cages and liberating them from airplanes, the eggs laid by females never hatched. In two years, the species was virtually wiped out in this area. Plant scientists have bred ability to resist insect damage into some crops. Also, entomologists concentrate on trying to breed weaknesses into injurious insects, so that they cannot survive.

Man may be holding his own against the insect menace, but no end to the war is yet in sight.

CHAPTER 11

Farmers
Protect a Heritage

In the spring of 1905, two young soil surveyors from Washington journeyed south to Louisa County, Virginia. The Department of Agriculture had sent them to find out why some of the land there, farmed for two centuries, had become so poor and unproductive. They saw the clay surface soil in the sloping fields, clay which baked in the sun and became hard as bricks. They saw, too, stretches of woodland where the plow had never been. Under the trees, the soil was loose and deep. Clearly the fields had once been covered with the same kind of good earth. When the trees had been chopped down and the fields plowed again and again, the rich topsoil had slowly washed away.

For one of these young men, this observation marked the beginning of an extraordinary career. During the next forty years, Hugh H. Bennett was to alert millions of farmers to the disastrous consequences of soil erosion. In time, he found ways to show them how to prevent such erosion, and with strong support from farmers and from his government, became the world-famous organizer of a great crusade for soil conservation.

Bennett and his associate were by no means the first to witness soil erosion. Men had long known that exposed soil would wash away. Thomas Jefferson, whose lands lay in the same Louisa County, had plowed around the slopes and hillsides, rather than up

85

and down, to lessen erosion. George Washington repeatedly urged his Mount Vernon farm managers to fill the gullies with cornstalks and brush, to keep the soil from washing away and help to restore the level of the fields. So, though in 1905 knowledge of erosion was widespread, nothing much was being done about it.

By the time Bennett visited Louisa County, the land policy of the United States government had produced the great expansion most people desired. United States lands from coast to coast had been opened to men eager to exploit the wealth that lay beneath the soil, within the forests and mines. For more than a hundred years, the country's natural resources had been exploited with aggressive vigor. If our resources were being wasted, few people worried; farther west there were plenty more, still untapped. Almost no one stopped to consider whether such apparently endless resources could be exhausted. The interdependence of forests, soils, water, and wildlife was little understood.

Originally, trees covered most of the Eastern third of the country. Historian James Truslow Adams said that a squirrel might have traveled from Maine to the mouth of the Mississippi by leaping from branch to branch, without ever touching the ground. Farm crops could not be grown under trees, so the first farmers were compelled to destroy the forest before they could plow fields. Millions of acres of virgin woods fell before the ax and saw. The trees were burned; there was no market for logs at that time.

With the trees gone, the plows pushed through the new fields and changes began to take place in the character of the land, changes little noticed at the time but of vital importance to future generations. For thousands of years, nature had been building up fertile soil under the trees. Nature needs a hundred years, it is said, to create one inch of topsoil. Through innumerable autumns the leaves had fallen and through innumerable summers they had decayed, while billions of insects and bacteria reduced them, along with the rotting wood of fallen trees, to loam and soil. When storms came and furious rains poured down, the branches and leaves broke the raindrops' fall; the litter on the ground combined with the tree roots to absorb the water, conserving millions of gallons. The forest shade delayed evaporation. Moisture was stored in the soil particles. Great quantities of water sank to make underground streams and reservoirs.

The farmer who plowed his new fields, after he had laboriously removed the trees and stumps, looked with well-earned pride upon his work. With the woods gone, he could raise wheat and corn and animals. He had done the necessary thing.

But no longer did trees break the fall of the rain. The forest floor had been turned under. No barrier stopped the water from forming little rills, as it sought to find its own level. The sun often baked the soil rock hard, so that less of the moisture could seep downward. The water rills were never clear and clean; they were roily, turbid with particles of soil that they carried with them down to the brooks, out to the rivers, and off to the sea.

What was happening? The precious topsoil was leaving the land, and for long years few realized how truly precious it was or how fast it was going. No one had pointed out that all mankind must forever depend for food upon the few inches of topsoil that nature had made little by little. Study hadn't yet disclosed that in North Africa and the Middle East millions now live in extreme poverty because their ancestors let the once rich topsoil wash away.

In some soils the rills that the rains made grew into gullies. These the farmer could easily see. If he took the trouble and acted in time, as George Washington urged his managers to do, he could prevent the gullies from spreading. How quickly they formed depended on the degree of slope in the fields and upon the kind of soil. One gully started from water dripping off the roof of the barn. In time, the barn fell in; the gully became two hundred-feet deep, undermined homes and schoolhouses, and eventually ruined a hundred thousand acres of land. Located in Stewart County, Georgia, the gully is known as Providence Cave. The eroded soil was carried by the Chattahoochee River into the Gulf of Mexico.

Sheet erosion in a South Dakota cornfield. Heavy rains have opened a deep gully.

A less spectacular, but more insidious form of soil disappearance is called *sheet* erosion. From bare land, with slopes so small as to seem almost level, the rains and melting snows carry with them tiny soil particles, as they make their inevitable way to lower levels. Spencer Logan's farm, and tens of thousands of others like it, was so slightly rolling that the difference in elevation between the highest and lowest spots was no more than ten feet. Spencer and many of his fellow farmers were puzzled, when they noticed that little knolls, once covered with black soil, began to turn yellow at the top. This yellow ground was hard-clay subsoil, and each year these areas grew larger. There, the cornstalks were thinner and the ears smaller. Not for a long time did Spencer and the other farmers learn that sheet erosion was carrying their farms, bit by bit, down into the drains and ditches, and away to the rivers.

On the great prairies where forests never grew, the rank grasses had for centuries performed the same role as the trees. Grass roots had restrained the run off of the rains. But, even though comparatively level, these lands, when plowed, also suffered their share of erosion. In floodtime, the swirling water, rushing downstream, often carried with it quantities of sand, gravel, and clay, which it deposited thickly, when the waters receded, over fertile lowland areas. When the flood diminished, the silt fell to the stream bottoms or built up at the mouths of rivers. Thus, the character of the stream was changed, and always for the worse. Harbors, for instance, sometimes become so filled with silt that they're no longer navigable to shipping.

Wind, as well as water, shares in the evil work of kidnaping fertile soil. After a lengthy drought, winds pick up the loosened dust from plowed fields and may carry it for long distances. And this dust in the wind brings us back to the story of Hugh H. Bennett, the man who made much of the world conscious of erosion.

A North Carolina farm boy, Bennett went to work for the United States Bureau of Soils in 1903. He had learned about gullies on his father's farm. So, in 1905, when he studied the field in Louisa County, Virginia, and compared its baked clay surface with the deep loam of the adjoining woodland, he realized that during many years of exposure, sheet erosion had carried away all the original topsoil. Soil surveying experience elsewhere—and there were few spots in America that he didn't visit sooner or later—convinced him that erosion was slowly destroying the nation's richest and most essential resource. But for many years, he could persuade neither his fellow scientists nor anyone else that the

menace he saw so clearly really existed. In fact, not until an arti-
cle he wrote on the subject appeared in a farm magazine in 1928
were his arguments taken seriously.

Then, in the spring of 1935, a dramatic hour came to
Bennett. He was testifying before a Senate committee in support
of a proposed act to establish a Soil Conservation Service, which
would conduct a national program for erosion control. Drought had
been taking its toll in several of the plains states. Bennett re-
minded the Senators of three dust storms the year before, vividly
describing how powder-dry soil from western Oklahoma had filled
the air as high as eight thousand feet and had darkened the sun as
far as the Atlantic coast, as it blew out to sea.

Each of these storms, he said, had probably carried not less
than 300,000,000 tons of fertile soil off the Great Plains, or about
150,000 acres of land twelve inches deep.

The attentive Senators were impressed. They listened closely,
as Bennett further explained how repeated plowing of the plains
had destroyed the grass that once held the soil in place, and how
the winds picked up the more valuable soil elements while leaving
behind the worthless sand and mineral fragments.

Then, as he talked, a strange thing happened. The room
began to darken. Bennett led the puzzled Senators to a window
and, looking out, they saw a pall of gritty dust covering Washington, dust from two thousand miles westward.

Bennett had known that the storm was actually on its way,
and had deliberately prolonged his testimony, counting on the
dust storm's arrival to dramatize and reinforce his argument. It did.
The soil conservation bill passed, and Bennett became the chief of
a vast national program designed to meet the huge challenge that
he had been first to recognize.

With generous governmental funds, plus his own limitless
energy, Bennett organized research and demonstration projects, to
show how soil could be saved. Only the farmers who owned and
tilled the land could prevent its erosion, and Bennett was de-

Wind erosion moves tons of fertile topsoil. The dust storms of the 1930's, originating in the drought-stricken areas of Oklahoma, Texas, and Kansas, sometimes darkened skies over Eastern cities before blowing out over the Atlantic.

termined to make them understand the urgency of conserving fertile soil within their farm boundaries, rather than letting it gradually disappear into the sea. His program was further extended when each of the states passed a uniform law authorizing the formation of Soil Conservation Districts.

From this point, soil-conservation programs moved more and more into the hands of farmers. The district organizations were initiated by farmers and are still controlled by them. When a farmer applies for help, a technician, provided by government, works out a plan suited to the farm's needs. They may include shaping fields by land contours, rather than in the usual rectangles; planting grasses or trees in certain areas; constructing ponds to store water for livestock, irrigation, or recreation; and other features.

More than 550 million acres had, by 1961, come under this kind of planning, and more are being added every year. More than 1,800,000 farmers and ranchers have participated. More than one

million new farm ponds have been built. No one can yet say that
the battle against soil erosion has been won, but farm owners are
beginning to win it. And they are making the soil-saving fight without government compulsion; their motive is self-interest, and
respect for the land itself. Government does the research and helps
make the plans.

Farmers' experience with preventing erosion made it clear
that conservation involved a great deal more than just topsoil. It
also involved ways of slowing the speed with which water moves
off the fields, after a rain. Restraining the water called for less
plowing and more grass or trees. This resulted in more "insoak,"
which in turn reduced the dangers of drought, because more
moisture was held underground for the roots of crop plants. Ponds
for water storage also became ponds in which to swim and fish.
The restored areas of grass and woodland brought back birds and

One of the many artificial ponds built by farmers.

U.S.D.A. photo

other wildlife, that had abandoned the clean, cultivated fields. Farmers became acquainted with a new word, *ecology*, the interdependent relationship between all forms of life and their environment.

The story is told of a wealthy man whose country estate included a small lake. He was particularly proud that pairs of wood ducks, the most beautiful of all American wild ducks, had raised their young on his lake. Then, one year, the wood ducks did not return. The owner called in a naturalist to find out why. The naturalist spent several days investigating.

"Your wood ducks have gone," he finally reported, "because your young son wanted a bicycle." The puzzled owner demanded an explanation.

"You told your son that when you were twelve years old and wanted a bicycle, you had to earn the money for it, and that it would be good for him to do the same," the naturalist answered. "The boy decided to earn the money by trapping skunks and selling their furs, so he trapped all the skunks in the neighborhood. The snapping turtles then multiplied fast in your lake, because the skunks no longer raided their nests and ate the eggs. Turtles, as you know, will swim under water and catch baby ducks. So, the wood ducks were smart enough to go somewhere else to raise their young." This story vividly illustrates the meaning of ecology, and its importance to us as individuals and as a nation.

The whole far-seeing concept of conservation grew from various and separate beginnings. For one, Theodore Roosevelt, while President of the United States (1901–1909), turned an idea into a national movement. Prompted by his friend, Gifford Pinchot, a rich Pennsylvanian who was the nation's first trained, scientific forester, and by others, Roosevelt preserved United States-owned forests from private exploitation, laid the basis for proper usage of water power and water for irrigation, and created new national parks. For another, the National Audubon Society, organized in 1905, has helped save from extinction several species of birds, such as the egret and roseate spoonbill; has created and administered great wildlife refuges; and worked continuously, through lectures, books, publicity, and summer camps, to teach conservation. And, the Isaac Walton League, especially interested in fishing and hunting, has done much to promote fish and game conservation. Increasingly, the different groups have found that their aims can best be served when the principles of ecology are observed. People who are concerned with soil conservation, water supply, forest growth, bird and game protection, prevention of water pollution, water power, recreation areas, and all other phases of conservation find their interests interwoven.

Theodore Roosevelt told an early conservation conference that while, in the past, we had "admitted the right of the individual to injure the future of the Republic for his own present profit, the time has come for a change." Farmers today know the deep truth of this. As owners of the soil on which they must make their own living, they realize that from the same soil, future generations must also be fed. The Americans of the next century will owe a great deal to men like Hugh Bennett and Theodore Roosevelt, who saw the need for conservation, and to the farmers of today, whose efforts are not only conserving the soil but all its related resources as well. Our twentieth-century farmers see themselves as temporary users of a heritage which must be preserved intact for those to follow.

CHAPTER 12   Education
                  Reaches Out

What is the single most necessary, most useful agricultural tool? The hoe? The spade? The plow? No. Information. Without correct information, farmers cannot make the best possible use of soil, of crops, or of livestock. Thus, the efforts of agricultural leaders to provide accurate information have been the foremost factor in the remarkable growth of American farm efficiency.

Progress in farming, as in every other field of human endeavor, stems from the minds of leaders. It has often been said that not more than one person in ten possesses the ability to manage the work of others. The proportion of real leaders must be even smaller, especially of those with the creative capacity to develop and pursue original ideas. American agriculture, fortunately, has produced leaders in farming, as well as leaders in many other fields.

George Washington was a farm leader, as well as a general and a president. Yet he had to educate himself in the arts of agriculture. He had to learn from mistakes and successes of his own and of his friends. In his time, there were no farm institutes, no county agents, no county fairs, no farm papers, no radio reports, no 4-H clubs, no vocational courses or agricultural colleges.

In his last message to Congress, Washington urged the creation of a federal board of agriculture, to gather and spread information and "to encourage and assist a spirit of discovery and improvement." Congress failed to vote on this wise proposal.

Thomas Jefferson, another great American, studied agricultural methods wherever he traveled in Europe, and sent home seeds and plants. After his retirement to Monticello, farming was his major interest.

Many other Revolutionary figures were also farm leaders. Between 1781 and 1795, such men organized at least six agricultural societies in various states. The Philadelphia Society for Promoting Agriculture, which began in 1785, with Benjamin Franklin as one of its members, still holds monthly meetings. These societies heard carefully prepared papers on farm experiences, many of which were printed and circulated for the benefit of others. Between 1800 and 1850, many small agricultural societies were organized for the exchange of information, mutual education, and for social purposes.

Individuals exerted influence by importing improved breeds of animals from Europe. Elkanah Watson, a Massachusetts businessman and a Merino sheep breeder, organized, at Pittsfield, what is regarded as the first agricultural fair. (Fairs are still centers where farming methods are shown.) Edmund Ruffin, the Virginia farmer who was said to have fired the first shot at Fort Sumter in 1861 and who then ended his own life at the defeat of the Confederacy, wrote and published extensively on better ways to improve the soil. John Taylor, another Virginian, a statesman, and farmer, wrote pamphlets and books to help his fellow farmers.

The early years of the Republic saw the beginnings of still another potent educational force. That was the agricultural press, which began its career in 1810 with a modest periodical called the *Agricultural Museum.* Farm publications multiplied through the years, until nearly every state and region had one. Journals sprang up devoted to poultry, dairy, goats, bees, and to individual breeds of livestock, all of them valuable sources of information—and also valuable for advertising products useful to farmers.

National farm periodicals didn't appear until the twentieth

century. When Wilmer Atkinson started the *Farm Journal* in 1877, he stated in the first issue that it was intended "for farmers living within a day's journey of Philadelphia," in other words for farmers in eastern Pennsylvania, New Jersey, Delaware, and northern Maryland. Today, air transportation enables his successors, who print more than three million copies monthly, to make the same statement about "a day's journey of Philadelphia."

The agricultural press, from its early times, has filled its columns with information useful to farmers in their business and in living. Surveys in recent years have repeatedly disclosed that, although other excellent communications media are active, most farmers look to favorite agricultural papers for their business information.

In the field of formal education, the name of Jonathan Turner is linked importantly to the story of American agriculture. During the decade preceding the Civil War, Turner—a native of Illinois—carried on a vigorous campaign for the establishment of colleges where agricultural and industrial arts would be taught. This was a radical concept in a period when institutions of higher learning were devoted primarily to classical subjects. In 1855, Michigan established Michigan State College; Pennsylvania in the same year created the Farmers High School, now called Pennsylvania State University. Turner won a strong supporter in Congress in the person of Justin Morrill, Representative from Vermont. After several unsuccessful tries, Morrill, in 1862, persuaded Congress to pass the Land-Grant College Act, which gave each state thirty thousand acres of public land for each Senator and Representative it had in Congress. From the proceeds of the sale of this land, the states were to set up colleges to teach subjects "related to agriculture and mechanic arts."

As the new land-grant colleges got under way after the Civil War, they found it difficult to develop practical agricultural courses. After setting up courses in geology, chemistry, and botany, the faculties wondered what else to teach. Most of the agricultural knowledge up to that time was purely practical in origin; it had been acquired by individual observation and by inheritance from previous generations. Much of this knowledge was sound, but some, such as rules for planting crops according to the phases of the moon, was subject to doubt. Consequently, colleges began to undertake experimental work. By 1887, fifteen of the new colleges had formally organized experiment stations. Impressed by the need for and the worth of these educational efforts, Congress, in that same year, passed the Hatch Act. This granted federal funds to help establish and operate experiment stations; six years later, forty-nine such stations had been set up in various states. The states provide most of the money now. Nearly every agricultural region has experimental farms, where crops and problems special to its area are under study.

Scientific knowledge of soils, crops, livestock, feeds, and farm procedures grew as the experimental work progressed and as more agricultural scientists were trained in the colleges. But, at the same time, this knowledge created another problem. It was not readily understood by farmers. The men who reported their experiment station finds were good scientists, but poor writers. Moreover, among older farmers, "book farmin" was in poor repute.

In several states, efforts were made to popularize improved farm techniques through Farmers' Institutes. A few community leaders organized a committee, arranged for a meeting place, and applied to the state for speakers. Normally, the Institute provided a two-day program in winter, when farmers had the leisure to attend. The staff of speakers, paid by the state, included specialists from the agricultural college or experiment station, along with farmers who were successfully using new methods and who were good at persuading an audience. The Institutes were useful and generally well attended, yet they were only able to do a sketchy job.

Then, in the early 1900's, an agricultural educator appeared who had a better idea. His name was Seaman A. Knapp. We have already met him in chapter nine. His plan was to persuade a few leading farmers in each county to apply the best practices known at their own expense. Other farmers, who saw the profitable results, he said, would adopt the improved methods. He had proved the value of this technique in the early fight against the cotton boll weevil.

The demonstration idea had far-reaching effects. While Knapp was preaching and proving it, President Theodore Roosevelt decided that something needed to be done to make farming and farm living more attractive and more profitable. He believed strongly in the importance of agriculture and of the farm home to the solidity of the nation. So, in 1908, he appointed a Country Life Commission, and named a distinguished scientist, writer, and educator, Dr. Liberty Hyde Bailey, as chairman. The Commission held hearings in various parts of the country, to learn what ideas farmers thought were most urgent. Its report resulted in several progressive steps. None was more important than the Smith-Lever Act, passed by Congress in 1914. It provided for the extension system, in which federal, state, and local funds could be employed to hire the farm and home demonstration agents, who now are found in practically every agricultural county. Knapp's idea still guides their work.

In 1917, Congress authorized another measure to make agricultural education available to more young people. The Smith-Hughes Act initiated federal help to high schools that wanted to offer practical agricultural courses, recognizing the fact that only a small proportion of farm boys could afford the time and money required to go on to an agricultural college.

Educators also became convinced that farming could be made more interesting to farm boys and girls by arranging for the youngsters to carry on actual outdoor projects as part of their studies. Encouraged by county-school superintendents, junior farm clubs sprang up in several Ohio, Illinois, and Iowa counties. When the members displayed the products of their work at school exhibits and at farm meetings, agricultural and school leaders saw that the new idea was sure to grow, and it did.

World War I, which started in Europe just before the agricultural extension system was begun, stimulated the demand for food, a demand that shot upward when the United States joined the war in 1917. The government, looking for ways to step up the output of foodstuffs, hastened to encourage organization of the boys' and girls' farm clubs on a national scale. The county agricultural agents took on the job.

Girls were invited into canning clubs, and boys into projects for raising garden and field crops, chickens, and livestock. The results were so good, and the clubs so popular, that no one thought of stopping them when the war emergency had passed. A name for them had come into use; they were called "4-H" clubs. The H's stand for head, heart, hands, and health. The emblem, a four-leaf clover, was suggested by O.H. Benson, an Iowa school superintendent. The 4-H motto is "To make the best better."

California 4-H boys watch an expert prepare a Hereford steer for exhibition.

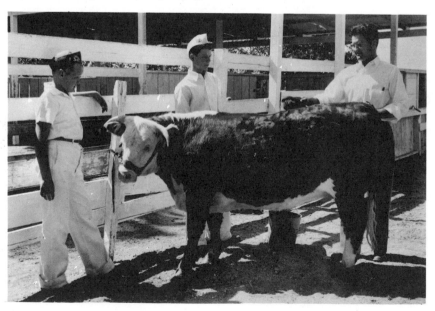

Here, two 4-H club members from Ohio display the lambs they have raised.

In fact, the practical values of 4-H work inspired a group of businessmen to organize a national committee to support it. The committee raises substantial funds, to provide outstanding 4-H students with scholarships, trips to Washington, and to big agricultural events. Competition among 4-H club members has become a leading feature at county and state fairs, and state winners receive trips to the International Livestock Exhibition in Chicago each year. This gathering of nearly two thousand bright boys and girls, in the week immediately following Thanksgiving, has become one of the most interesting and impressive annual agricultural events. From tiny beginnings in a few local schools, 4-H has grown until more than 1,500,000 boys and girls take part each year.

The age range of 4-H members is from eleven to twenty-one years. Each club has its volunteer adult leader, a man or woman who supervises the club meetings and helps the members develop their projects. While the clubs in most counties are under the general supervision of the agricultural agent, in hundreds of counties the work is so highly regarded that a special club agent devotes his entire time to 4-H work.

Another important agricultural youth organization is the Future Farmers of America. Open only to boys who attend vocational agricultural high schools, members are active until they reach twenty-one. F.F.A. differs from 4-H not only in its all-boy membership, but in procedure. Usually, each boy undertakes an individual project, which he pursues as long as he is a member and which may turn out to be his major life work. The project may be growing a particular kind of livestock or a particular crop. He keeps careful records and writes reports on his work and earnings. Indeed, many an F.F.A. project has helped a boy to save several thousand dollars by his twenty-first birthday.

F.F.A. members are organized into school or community chapters, where they learn parliamentary procedure and public speaking. They are trained not only in farming, but in useful citizenship as well. Frequently, the chapters undertake special services for the communities, such as inspecting buildings and machinery for safety, rat extermination, planting or maintaining a community F.F.A. forest. All this is in line with their motto: "Learning to Do, Doing to Learn: Earning to Live, Living to Serve."

The chapters set up state organizations with state officers. Once a year, in October, F.F.A. delegates from all over the country attend a huge national convention in Kansas City. Here, there is active rivalry to win election as a national officer. Competition is equally keen for the "Star Farmer of America" awards, based on achievements in farming and in community service.

Through the 4-H clubs and the F.F.A., hundreds of thousands of farm youths have taken part in stimulating activities. They have learned, by seeing and doing, that scientific methods produce more and better crops, livestock, and poultry. Probably a majority of today's farmers were once members or have had children who were members of one of these organizations; and one result is that the old prejudice against "book farming" has almost completely disappeared. The present-day farmer not only believes in science, but watches avidly for new findings to apply in his business. He knows something about soil chemistry, the science of animal nutrition, genetics, and the many other sciences which are pertinent to his particular kind of farming.

Of the graduates from the four-year agricultural colleges, only about fifteen per cent return to the land to farm. The others either go into industries serving agriculture or become county agents, "Vo-Ag" teachers, or scientists in one of the many agricultural fields. Whatever their future plans, young farm people these days reach maturity prepared to make the most of the many opportunities which their agricultural education will bring to them.

CHAPTER 13

Too Many
and Too Much

For a full hundred years, between 1790 and 1890, America's farmers moved ever westward, as we have seen, over the vast spaces from the Atlantic to the Pacific. Wherever fertile soils and green pastures were to be found, farmers had settled. The prospect for the future seemed bright. As it turned out, tremendous progress was ahead; and also great difficulties and huge problems.

A nationwide business depression in the first half of the 1890's made it hard for farmers to get ahead. But in those days, they still raised their own power, their own fuel, and their own food; even with low incomes they could stay in business. The depression lifted, prices improved, and, until 1920, agriculture was prosperous.

Then came the beginnings of the biggest, toughest problem farmers have ever faced: the problem of surpluses, too much wheat, too much corn, too much cotton! Soon, new questions were to be asked. Were there also too many farmers—and too much land being farmed?

The story of surpluses is full of contradictions. Let's look at what happened to people who were farming, and what happened to the farms themselves. Then we shall see why farmers have produced so much of certain crops that the surplus is not just a farm problem, but a serious national burden.

The truth, which many farm spokesmen dislike facing, is that there have long been too many farmers. As long as homesteads were free or good land was cheap, farming attracted men who wanted to be independent. Farmers were praised as "the backbone of the nation," and farming was usually regarded as a way of life rather than as a business.

Much could be said to support these views. Although the life was often terribly hard, it was secure. The farmer, who owned his land, had no boss. He made his own plans and his own decisions. He was free to take a day off when he wanted to go fishing or visit the county fair. The farm was an excellent place for children; they had the whole outdoors as a playground, pets among the young animals, and at an early age were given chores to do that developed a sense of responsibility.

The same was true for those who did not own land, but rented from others, expecting in time to be able to purchase their own farms, as thousands did. Counted in the farm population, too, were large numbers of laborers who worked by the day or month, in many instances supplied with a house, garden, and other advantages. Their cash wages were low, but, as did owners and renters they liked the way of life. Usually they had no training for industrial or business jobs, and no liking for the restrictions of town or city living.

Farmers made up about one-third of the nation's total population in the 1890–1910 period. Forty years later, the 1960 census revealed that only a little more than one-twelfth—8.7%—of the people were farmers. While city populations had grown enormously, the number of farming people fell. So, too, did the number of farms. This number hovered just above six million, from 1910 until 1943. Since then it has gone down to four million. And, from the economic viewpoint, that may still be too many.

Here we encounter one of the big contradictions: fewer farmers and not so many farms; a great many more city people, yet too much food.

Those first years of the twentieth century were good years for farmers; expenses were not high and prices were steady. "These were our golden years," farmers like Spencer Logan said. The demand for wheat during World War I induced men to plow up thousands of semiarid acres on the Great Plains. But after the war, prices collapsed. Many who had expected prosperity to continue found themselves deeply in debt for machinery and land. Europe was poor, and no longer could buy as much pork and grain as formerly, while we had more to sell. Now, for the first time, the word *surplus* attached itself to the agricultural vocabulary. Although in the 1920's American businessmen prospered, farmers did not.

Next came the worldwide depression of the 1930's. Twelve million Americans lost their jobs. Business made little profit. Not only did foreign food demand lessen, but city people were on relief or bought only the food they needed in order to live. Farmers had to keep producing to meet their taxes and other obligations. So *surplus* became more troublesome than ever.

Sharp changes, in fact, a whole new agricultural era, began with the outbreak of World War II, in 1939, and the United States' entrance into the war in late 1941. The surpluses that had accumulated swiftly disappeared. Farmers were told that: "Food Will Win the War and Make the Peace." The government promised that good prices would be maintained for two years after a peace treaty was signed. With patriotic enthusiasm, farmers produced what their country asked, and they were well paid.

The biggest changes in agriculture, during and since World War II, were the adoption of greatly improved machinery, the huge increases in use of fertilizers, and the better scientific control of insects and crop diseases. All of these affected the numbers of people needed on farms, changed the size of farms, and played their parts in the surplus picture.

High wartime wages attracted thousands of farm laborers to the big cities, where most of them remained. After the war's end, manufacturing industries built many new plants near smaller cities. Farmers with little land found that they could make better livings on factory payrolls than on their small farms, yet not have to move to an unfamiliar city environment. They could continue to live in their homes, while renting or selling the land to farmers who wanted to enlarge their holdings. Some found opportunities to set up businesses of their own, to serve the increasing populations in their home areas.

The tractor and its auxiliary equipment worked in two ways to make farms bigger. Because it was faster than horses, had more power, and could work longer hours, a farmer needed more land to make full use of the tractor; because it was expensive, he needed to produce more to make the investment profitable. So the farmers who wanted to take town jobs or wanted to retire found buyers for their land. Back in the horse-and-mule days, the average-sized farm had about a hundred and fifty acres; now the average is more than three hundred acres, more than double.

Tractors and power machinery by themselves do not increase the yield of crops, except perhaps as they provide better plowing

A six-row machine like this can plant either corn or cotton, and can apply fertilizer at the same time. The fertilizer is deposited a little deeper than the seed and in continuous bands alongside.

U.S.D.A. photo

and cultivation. But by replacing animal power, they made their contribution to the surplus problem.

The "fuel" for horses and mules had always been grown on the farm. Each animal required nearly two acres for the hay, grain, and pasture to feed it. The country's horse and mule population consumed the produce of between forty-five and fifty million acres. The acres that once fed horses gradually became available for the feeding of people.

Even with these acres added to food lands, farmers might have done no more than kept up with the growing demands from the rapidly rising urban populations. But two other factors must still be considered.

Before World War II, artificial fertilizers were not widely used. Most soils, after a few years of raising crops, were depleted of certain elements essential to plant growth, and their yields declined. The most important of these elements are phosphorus, potash, and nitrogen. Phosphorus in abundance could be obtained from fossil deposits in Florida, Tennessee, and Idaho. Potash sources are located in the Southwest.

Nitrogen, however, was long a costly element to obtain, even though the air over a single square mile of surface is estimated to contain twenty million tons of it. In 1914, German scientists discovered a process by which the atmospheric nitrogen could be extracted. Eventually a cheap nitrogen fertilizer was developed, and because nitrogen is an essential part of protein, the quality of many crops improved. It is also a stimulant to growth, and enabled farmers to produce more than ever before.

Manufacturers combine the three elements of phosphorus, potash, and nitrogen in the desired proportion and sell the product to farmers in burlap bags as fertilizer.

There were still other developments during these years, which help to explain the surplus problem. Farmers adopted hybrid corn, and the greater vigor of its seed added ten bushels an acre to the average corn yield. Better seed strains increased yields of other

Airplanes, especially designed for the purpose, spread chemical insecticides on growing crops.

crops. New chemical insecticides and pesticides, as we have seen, help to prevent crop failures. Irrigation became more common. Even in the East and Midwest, where rainfall is usually plentiful, farmers began to insure their crops against drought by installing irrigation systems, supplied with water from streams, ponds, and wells.

During World War II, price-support laws were put in force and then were continued after the war ended. These supports practically guaranteed the producers of wheat, cotton, rice, peanuts, tobacco, and corn against financial loss. The supports were in the form of loans to farmers who agreed to limit certain specified crops, but the limitations were never made drastic enough to reduce the output.

Farmers did the natural thing. They limited their plantings of the supported and restricted crops, and grew something else on the remaining acres, usually their poorest land. The guaranteed-price crops not only were planted on the best land, but received far more of the new fertilizers. As a result, yields per acre increased so much that the acreage restrictions did little to reduce the actual output. However, the guaranteed prices kept farmers from changing to other crops or seeking different sources of income, as they would have done in response to the demands of a free market. Year after year, huge quantities of wheat, corn, and cotton poured into the government storehouses, and eventually became the property of the government. Now, while a government

The vast wheat harvest in the Great Plains begins in Texas and moves northward with the season into Saskatchewan. Fleets of self-propelled combines move with the harvest, fulfilling contracts with farmers who find it cheaper to hire combines than to tie up capital in machines used only for a brief period each year.

U.S.D.A. photo

can easily buy products, it can sell them only with great difficulty because of the political pressures exerted to protect markets both at home and abroad. The United States found that it could not even give away, except in great emergencies, foodstuffs which hungry populations abroad needed badly. Competing producer nations considered gifts or bargain sales unfair to them, and had their diplomats tell us so.

Thus we can see that agricultural surpluses, despite fewer farmers, fewer farms, and a growing population, have resulted from many different factors, aggravated and encouraged by unwise legislation, which may have actually done the farmers and the country more harm than good.

The number of farmers will probably decline for some years to come. Nine-tenths of the farm products which go to market are sold from less than half of the farms. This means that more than half of the farms, about two million, sell only one-tenth of the total agricultural output. So, it's logical to expect that many of these low-producing farms will have to go out of business, or be absorbed by larger operators, or will themselves become larger operations. Great numbers of these small producers, though counted in the census as farmers, earn comfortable incomes from other work. In fact, many work off the farm at forty-hour-a-week jobs and manage to raise crops or livestock in their spare time. They're known as "time-and-a-half" farmers.

Will there always be too many farmers? Well, we've had a glimpse in this chapter of what the successful farmer of today has to be: a man with a big operation, who uses efficient machinery and scientific methods of agriculture. In the years ahead, those who are not capable managers, or who cannot find enough capital, will not try to farm.

And will there always be surpluses? We have no new land. We have more people every year to feed. At some point in the years ahead, we'll have so many people that surpluses will be no problem. But no one knows when that day will come.

CHAPTER 14   # Farmers
                 Join Hands

Farmers in America have always been accustomed to helping each other. When a settler in the wilderness set out to build a cabin, he could cut and bring together the logs by himself. He needed help, though, to lift and fit them all into place. Later, after the sawmills came and could cut the lumber for a barn, he needed plenty of willing hands to raise the frame. Then, when the steam-threshing machines arrived, neighbors came from several farms to help. The settler, in turn, helped them.

Exchange of work was an early form of coöperation among farmers. Some tasks became social events, such as the old-time "husking bee." The cornstalks were piled in the barn. Men, women, and children crowded in to husk the ears, and the lucky youth who found a red ear among the white and yellow ones got to kiss the girl of his choice.

For farmers to organize on a large scale for business purposes was a long step from neighborly barn-raising. Mistakes, failures, and disappointments occurred frequently, but powerful and useful organizations have emerged.

Probably the very first coöperative business ventures by farmers were the mutual fire-insurance societies. These operated simply. If a member's thousand dollar barn burned down, and the society had two hundred members, each was required to pay five dollars; the man who suffered the fire then received the money to rebuild his barn. A city group had pioneered this idea in 1752, when Benjamin Franklin headed the board of directors of the "Philadelphia Contributorship for the Insurance of Houses from Loss by Fire," which is still in business.

Then there were the five Wisconsin farmers who made their milk into cheese. They discovered that one of the five knew how to make much better cheese than the others, cheese which brought a higher market price. The farmers banded together and took all their milk to the expert, who made and sold the cheese and returned to each his share of the money. This arrangement came to be called a "cheese ring." Because it worked so well, dozens of other dairy groups adopted the idea. Near Rome, New York, in 1851, a coöperative cheese factory was set up. Eventually hundreds of such factories, owned and managed by farmers, spread over New York State, New England, Wisconsin, and elsewhere.

Such pioneering efforts in business organization inspired farmers to attempt to buy and sell many other products coöperatively. Their first purpose was to obtain for themselves the profits which went to "middlemen." They didn't want to pay someone else for doing jobs they believed they could do for themselves.

The farm coöperative, as it was worked out by many experiences, follows a few simple principles. One is that each member has one vote and only one vote, regardless of how much he buys or sells. Another is the "patronage dividend." When a member buys from his coöperative, he pays the usual retail price. At the end of the year he gets a refund check or dividend, which represents the profit the coöperative has saved for him. Sometimes part of the profit is held back to enlarge the coöperative; then the individual member is given a certificate, showing his share of the ownership. When he sells through the coöperative, he is paid whatever his products brought, less his share of the cost of selling them.

Coöperative associations vary in size from small local groups to multimillion dollar concerns. And they are now recognized in our country as one of the four principle ways of doing business, the others being by a private individual, by a partnership, and by a corporation. The original investment for an agricultural coöperative is put up by the organizing farmers, who are sometimes aided by loans from the federal Bank for Coöperatives.

For an example of a highly successful coöperative, let's look to southern California. The pioneers who began growing oranges there in the 1870's and 1880's found that harvesting a fine crop was easy enough, but making a profit was hard. Their markets were a long distance to the east. Dishonest Eastern fruit dealers sometimes sold carloads of fruit, kept the proceeds, and sent the grower a bill for freight. On the other hand, local fruit buyers agreed to stay out of each other's territories and not to compete, thus keeping prices low. So, whether he sold at home or shipped to the Eastern commission men, the grower was likely to be disappointed.

Not to be defeated, the orange producers began to organize coöperative selling groups, by-passing the commission men entirely. Their successes eventually outnumbered their failures, and gradually the coöperative won wide acceptance among citrus farmers—yet another instance of stubborn American determination. Now, California citrus growers market three-fourths of their fruit through their wholly owned coöperative, Sunkist Growers, Inc. All the grading, packing, shipping, advertising, and selling is done coöperatively. They maintain research laboratories, handle supplies for members, keep sales offices open both here and abroad, and sell a total of more than 220 million dollars worth of citrus products a year.

At the opposite side of the country we find another illustration of solid coöperative success. About 1920, New York State farmers decided that they were tired of having to buy dairy and poultry feeds that were adulterated, seeds that were not always as good as represented, and fertilizers that cost too much. So they started the G.L.F. Exchange. The name was taken from the initials of the state Grange, Dairymen's League, and Farm Bureau

This office building in Los Angeles is owned by California farmers, who market "Sunkist" oranges and other citrus fruit products.

Federation, the three organizations whose leaders drew the plans. The G.L.F., now a 175 million dollar business, owns feed mills and fertilizer-mixing plants, handles gasoline and fuel oil, and sells other supplies to members from convenient stores. It markets eggs, grains, beans, and other produce for members. Similar purchasing coöperatives operate in several other states. Through them, members may also obtain automobile, life, fire, and medical insurance.

A special form of coöperation is practiced by producers of milk. For each hundred pounds of milk they sell most dairy owners contribute two cents to a promotion fund, which amounts to eight million dollars a year. This money buys advertising to remind people to drink three glasses of milk every day, hires scientists to study the food values of dairy products, and employs people to

The Dairymen's League, a New York state coöperative, ships fresh milk to cities in tank trucks emblazoned with its "Dairylea" brand. The four-thousand-gallon tank is a single piece of plastic.

work with other food industries to promote milk consumption. Livestock farmers give to a similar fund to promote meats.

More than a fifth of all farm products are sold through coöperative effort, and about a sixth of all farm supplies are coöperatively purchased.

So far we have been talking about the way farmers have worked together, to buy and sell. They also work together in important national groups, which are known as the "general" farm organizations. There are three of these: the National Grange, the National Farmers Union, and the American Farm Bureau Federation.

The first man who attempted to organize farmers on a big scale was Oliver Hudson Kelley, a Minnesota farmer, who had a Washington, D. C., job in the Bureau of Agriculture. After two trips around the country on business for the Bureau in 1865–1866, Kelley became convinced that farmers needed an organization. With Washington acquaintances, he drew up plans for a secret, fraternal order, which they called the National Grange of Patrons of Husbandry. In 1868, Kelley began setting up local units in the Middle West, but at first progress was slow. He ran out of money, and had to borrow to return to his Minnesota farm. His persistence, however, and the farmers' growing discontent were soon to bring results. By 1874, more than twenty thousand local Granges had been organized, most of them in the Midwest and South.

With an agricultural depression coming on at this period, farmers used their Grange meetings to thrash out their problems and grievances. Their resentment of high railroad rates, high interest charges, speculators, high tariffs, and other evils was aired. While the National Grange was not political in intent, it could not prevent members from meeting to push political action. In fact, in a number of states, political forces allied with the new farm organization elected candidates to state legislatures. As a result, several Midwestern states passed laws to regulate railroad rates. Most of these laws were loosely drawn and did not stand up in the courts, which were more sympathetic to the railroads than to the farmers. Nevertheless, the principle of regulating rates in the public interest was established, and eventually the railroads came under federal supervision through the Interstate Commerce Act.

Today the National Grange has some eight thousand community units. It is most influential in the East and Northwest. National headquarters are in Washington, D. C. The Grange, incidentally, was the first secret order to admit women as equal members with men.

The Great Plains states—Montana and the Dakotas to Oklahoma and Texas—provide the most support for the National Farmers Union. This organization, with a main office in Denver, fosters large-grain marketing and other kinds of farm coöperatives.

The largest of the farm organizations, American Farm Bureau Federation, sprang into being shortly after World War I. Experiences during the war had convinced farmers that their problems were not well understood by leaders in business and in government, nor by city populations. Many farmers felt that what was needed was a powerful organization to work out ways and means to improve the marketing of agricultural products. Thus, early in 1919, farm leaders from a dozen states met at Ithaca, New York, to discuss just such a new national organization. In Chicago, a few months later, a larger group put together the framework of the organization, and elected an Iowa farmer, James R. Howard, as president.

"The East and the West, the North and the South, have agricultural problems which are different only in their external aspects," President Howard told the organizers. "These problems are basically similar or identical. We need to create a national spirit in our agricultural life."

Membership in the Federation grew rapidly. About 1,750,000 families are now Farm Bureau members, and forty-nine states and Puerto Rico are represented. Only Alaska is not a member.

The farmers' plea for better returns from their marketing led the Federation, as one of its first tasks, to form coöperative marketing associations. A large-scale grain marketing corporation was tried, but failed to influence prices and was dissolved. There were other failures. Successes, however, were numerous and important. Practical improvements were achieved in coöperative livestock selling. Through a joint effort with power companies, electric service was extended to more than a million farms before 1936, when the Rural Electrification Administration was established by the government. Exercising its influence with Congress, the Federation obtained laws which were helpful to farmers.

Farm prosperity, during the 1920's, was intermittent and spotty. But the fall in prices of farm products, during the worldwide depression of the 1930's, was much more serious, and for many farmers the effects were tragic. During these and the World War II years, the Farm Bureau Federation was concerned mainly with getting Congress to pass laws that would help agriculture, and with protecting farm interests in the numerous administrative agencies.

Unfortunately, the emphasis on legislation led to postwar difficulties over the mounting surpluses. Farm Bureau members recognized this. Allan Kline, the Iowa hog farmer who became national Farm Bureau president in 1947, reflected the views of many members when he said: "Our farm program must be consistent with the general welfare . . . and must safeguard . . . the great productive potentialities in the free American system." His successor, Charles B. Shuman, of Illinois led the organization toward what he called "freedom from compulsion." The Farm Bureau, in recent years, has vigorously opposed government controls in agriculture, has fought against high price supports, and has advocated a policy of discontinuing subsidies whether for farmers or for others.

The state Farm Bureau organizations have established many coöperative business services for their members, ranging from insurance to sale of products. The national Farm Bureau has set up an office in Rotterdam, Holland, to search out European buyers for American farm products. Among the results of this plan was that one of the first ships to go out the new St. Lawrence seaway carried a cargo of frozen turkeys, sold to Germany, by a North Dakota Farm Bureau coöperative.

Despite their business and legislative successes, farmers still are far from presenting a united front. Although the Farm Bureau opposes government interference with production and prices, the National Farmers Union favors even greater intervention by government, while the National Grange takes a position somewhere between the two.

The men who operate the four million farms in our country may agree that they want better, more stable incomes. But they do not agree on how to get them, thus reflecting the independent and individualistic spirit which has always characterized American farmers.

CHAPTER 15   Government
Helps and Hinders

Just fifty years after Washington's first inauguration, Henry L. Ellsworth, the son of the third Chief Justice of the United States, persuaded Congress for the first time to provide money for agricultural purposes. In 1839, he obtained an appropriation of one thousand dollars, and from this small beginning grew the huge Department of Agriculture of today.

For several years, the work was carried on under the supervision of the Patent Office where Henry Ellsworth was the Commissioner. Eventually, appropriations rose to thirty-five thousand dollars annually. A chemist, a botanist, and an entomologist were employed. Then, in 1862, President Lincoln signed a law which gave agriculture the status of an independent government bureau. Successive commissioners improved the Bureau's work, and, in 1882, the first "Farmers' Bulletins" were issued. In time, these brief pamphlets came to cover a multitude of subjects investigated by the Bureau, and to serve as an important educational medium.

The livestock and dressed-meat industries grew rapidly in the 1870's, shipping large quantities of meat across the Atlantic. When England and nations on the continent began to restrict their imports because they said much American meat came from diseased animals, Congress responded by establishing a Bureau of Animal

120

Industry, with strong regulatory powers. The Bureau set up quarantine stations and initiated a vigorous research effort, which put an end to pleuro-pneumonia and Texas fever, the two most destructive cattle ailments. The scientist who did this research, Dr. Theobald Smith, found that ticks carried the germs causing Texas fever, a discovery that not only helped to conquer cattle fever, but opened the way to later discoveries that germs borne by insects transmit bubonic plague, malaria, yellow fever, typhus, African sleeping sickness, and other diseases which assail human beings.

When the editor of a Missouri farm paper, Norman J. Colman, became Commissioner of Agriculture in 1885, he strongly supported the growing demand for federal help to agricultural research. Congress, in 1887, approved the law which appropriated public funds for experiment stations in each state. Then, in 1889, just fifty years after Henry Ellsworth obtained the first agricultural appropriation, and an even century after the government began, the Department of Agriculture was given full executive status, and Colman, its first Secretary, took his seat in the President's cabinet.

Government took another step for farmers in 1896, when it established free rural delivery of mail. Until then, farmers had to travel to the nearest post office, although city people had long enjoyed door-to-door delivery. Within a few years after the first rural free delivery routes were set up, the service reached farms all over the nation. Farmers were able to subscribe to daily newspapers, thus keeping more closely in touch with markets and the news of the world.

Like carrying the mail, money is a function of government. Through many periods since the colonial era, the special characteristics of agriculture had raised problems of money and credit. As raw-material producers, competing with each other in large numbers, farmers were unable to control their prices or to withhold their perishable products from market. Land speculation, fluctuations in value of currency, crop failures, and slow turnover, which results from the months or years that elapse between seeding or breeding and eventual sales, frequently combined to place farmers at a disadvantage. The banking system was not well adapted to meet rural needs for long-term credit, either to purchase and pay for land, to mature crops, or to finance ventures in livestock.

The Federal Farm Loan Act, established by Congress in 1916, initiated a better system of farm credit. It was developed in several steps, and has, in general, been very successful. Parts of it are now wholly owned by farmer members. Private banking institutions, in order to compete, have improved their loan services to farmers.

Until after World War I, agriculture had really demanded very little from government. Scientific research, some educational measures, regulation of railroads, mail delivery, a better credit system, these were about all. But in 1920, when the inflated war prices suddenly collapsed, the farmers needed help—and needed it quickly. Before the end of the next year, corn had fallen from $1.85 a bushel to 91 cents, wheat from $2.58 to 92 cents, hogs from 19 cents a pound to 6½ cents, and other products in proportion.

Farmers had experienced depressions before. They had recovered largely by tightening their belts and spending less. But now, the situation had changed. Debts, greater than ever before, required cash; so did equipment. Unlike horses, automobiles could not be kept going on an extra forkful of hay.

While financial distress spread in the farm areas, with many farmers going bankrupt, finance, manufacturing, and commerce generally were prosperous. Outside of the rural sections, few realized the seriousness of the situation. Politicians from agricultural districts, however, were well aware of it. Conferences and commissions met in Washington to study the problem, but no one saw any clear solution.

Meanwhile, in Congress, a "farm bloc," made up of Senators and Representatives from farm states, began to attract attention. Ignoring party lines and standing together on farm issues, the "bloc" held a balance of power in both houses. Measures were passed, which liberalized credit to farmers, imposed new regulations upon traders in grain, forbade discriminatory practices at central stockyards, and permitted farm coöperatives to operate without being subject to the antitrust laws.

In 1929, the new President, Herbert Hoover, proposed plans for stabilizing agricultural prices. Congress adopted his plan for a Federal Farm Board and provided a $500,000,000 fund for its operation. The Board immediately set up a division to encourage coöperative marketing, with some results that proved permanently valuable.

The Great Depression, which settled over the world in 1929 and 1930, however, swept farm prices to new lows. Even the half-billion-dollar fund, which seemed to be a huge sum at that time, wasn't enough to buy and hold crops to bolster the markets. Both business and agriculture were deep in an economic slump when Franklin D. Roosevelt became president in March, 1933.

The continuing urgency of the farm situation was dramatized by occasional violence. At a mortgage foreclosure sale in South Dakota, the attorney for owners of the mortgage was seized by sympathetic farmers and held prisoner until the sale was postponed. In Pennsylvania, another sale was posponed after three deputy sheriffs were roughed up. Wisconsin and New York dairy farmers tried vainly to get better prices rcfusing to deliver their milk. Iowa farmers forcibly removed a county judge from his bench, after he insisted that it was his duty to sign mortgage foreclosure orders; and martial law was declared for some counties by the governor, who feared that threats and turbulent feelings would excite mob violence.

It was generally believed that overproduction was the principal cause of farm distress. Early in May, 1933, Congress passed a law authorizing the Secretary of Agriculture to require farmers to restrict planted acreage to certain crops. The law also authorized the levy of a tax on the manufacturers who processed these

crops, thus providing funds to compensate farmers for not producing. By June, the Agricultural Adjustment Administration, soon
to be known as the "Triple A," had issued decrees, fixing the
processing taxes and arranging for thousands of government agents
to explain the new programs to farmers.

The most spectacular action followed in August. The Secretary of Agriculture, Henry A. Wallace, attempted to raise prices by
killing pigs and plowing under growing cotton. This was an unprec-
edented idea. Despite many protests, the government offered more
than double the prevailing market price for young pigs in the twenty-
five- to seventy-five-pound range. (Hogs normally are marketed
after they weigh two hundred pounds or more.) Four million pigs
were sold, and most of them turned into fertilizer by the packing
plants; more than two hundred thousand sows, for which farmers
got a bonus of four dollars over the market price, met the same
fate. The government paid out more than $34,000,000 for the ex-
periment, but hog prices did not rise. The government also
paid more than $700,000,000 to farmers for plowing up some
10,000,000 acres of the 1933 cotton crop.

Every farm county soon had its paid local committee, whose
duty it was to decide how many acres farmers could plant in the
principal crops, to see that agreements were complied with, and to
figure out the checks which were sent to farmers for reducing their
production.

Then, in 1936, the United States Supreme Court declared the
processing tax, which provided the money for these schemes, to be
unconstitutional. Congress had no power, the Court said, to try to
regulate agricultural production directly, and none to attempt to do
so indirectly through payments which, in effect, were coercive.

Congress promptly passed the Soil Conservation and Domestic
Allotment Act of 1936. This law provided a half-billion dollars for
the Secretary of Agriculture to use in making payments to farmers
for observing certain soil-conserving practices, with emphasis on
shifting away from the "soil-depleting" crops, which happened to

be those in greatest surplus. By this legal subterfuge, crop reduction was made incidental to soil conservation.

Thousands of farmers refused, as a matter of principle, to accept the government's payments "for doing," as they said, "what we ought to do anyhow, take care of our soil." These, however, were a minority.

The payments were helpful to many others, even though neither agriculture nor business recovered from the depression until the outbreak of World War II in 1939. Then, war preparations and demands from abroad swiftly changed the picture. When the United States entered the conflict in December, 1941, it was realized that food would become the most essential of war matériel.

A new law guaranteed that prices would be maintained for at least two years after a treaty of peace had been signed. This provision was to cause unforeseen trouble, since after the war, politicians in both parties were afraid to reduce these price supports. Today, under the law, farmers can put their grain or cotton in government storage, and receive a loan which may prove to be even higher than market prices. In this case, the government becomes owner of the commodity. If prices do go higher, farmers can withdraw the product and sell it on the open market.

Consequently, despite all efforts to reduce acreage and production, and despite all efforts to sell and even give away the government holdings, nearly every year, since 1946, has brought a new surplus of wheat, corn, and cotton. By 1960, these holdings had reached the huge total of ten billion dollars' worth, and today no solution to the problem is in sight.

CHAPTER 16

Freedom and Abundance

Land and freedom! The young United States had both to offer in greater abundance than ever before in the history of any single nation. The American land extended from "sea to shining sea"—the full breadth of the continent.

To the emigrant, the rich and tempting expanses of the United States exerted a powerful attraction. Land meant opportunity. Yet there were some who made the long and fateful journey from the old country to the new, who saw beyond the purely material rewards of land and opportunity. They saw ahead of them the priceless gift of freedom. Few of these courageous emigrants had ever known the right of choice as Americans knew it. They were to learn its blessings and its responsibilities.

From ten thousand emigrants in 1825, the number rose to a high of over a million in 1907. The land-hungry came in largest numbers during the last half of the nineteenth century.

Wherever farmers took up new lands, towns invariably grew up in their wake. Alert to business opportunities, men who needed no one's permission opened general stores, selling groceries, clothing, and equipment to farmers. Other buyers came to purchase the grain, livestock, wool, hides, or whatever produce the farmers had to sell. At the crossroads, railroad stop, or river bend, where the grocer and the produce buyer established themselves, a sawmill was usually set up. Before long, there came a blacksmith and a shoe-maker, a harness maker, tailor, dry-goods merchant, carpenter, mason, barber, doctor, and lawyer, who, with their families, needed schools and teachers. As the towns grew, they attracted a newspaper, a bank, a drug store, and a jeweler's shop. In time, someone started an ice plant, and if suitable clays were nearby, a brick-and-tile factory. Each business served its neighbors in the town, as well as the farmers in the surrounding countryside. Competitors arrived to open new stores; clerks and bookkeepers found jobs. Another American town was booming.

These town enterprises had to send to larger centers to obtain the goods they sold. As the little farm towns multiplied and were added to, the city wholesale centers expanded. New factories were built, to make the goods that the wholesalers distributed to retailers many miles away. Thus America grew. And agriculture was its base.

Today, nearly forty per cent of the nation's business is related to agriculture. To see how, you only need to look into the stores of the nearest downtown shopping area. There is food, of course, in the groceries, meat stores, restaurants, and hotels; there is clothing, made of cotton, wool, linen, or rayon. Even nylon uses a chemical called furfural, which comes from either corncobs or oat hulls. There is leather in the shoes; linseed (flaxseed) oil and casein in the paints. Tobacco, paper products, and many of the drugs are farm-grown. Wherever you look along Main Street, U.S.A., except perhaps in the jewelry and antique shops or some of the hardware stores, you will find products stemming directly or indirectly from the farms.

In fact, so vital is agriculture to the whole economy that a special term, *agribusiness,* has come into use. It describes the economic activity which arises from processing, transporting, and distributing products of the soil, or from preparing and selling the materials consumed by farmers.

Another comparatively new word in our vocabulary is

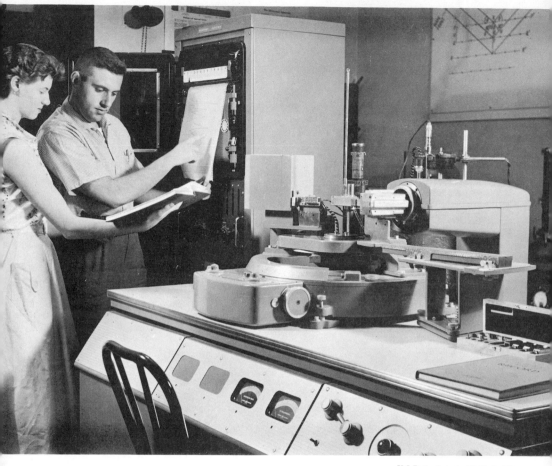

U.S.D.A. photo by M. C. Audsley

Science goes to work for agriculture. Here X-ray diffraction apparatus is used to determine the properties of plastics made from animal fats.

chemurgy, which means putting chemistry and other sciences to work for agriculture. In its more restricted sense, chemurgy concerns the development of new non-food uses for farm-grown raw materials, and the establishment of new crops primarily for non-food purposes. Traditionally, farmers have dealt in foods and fibers. Modern industry, however, utilizes such chemical raw materials as starch, proteins, sugar, oils, and cellulose, all constituents of plants. Scientific research has not yet fully explored the possibilities of plants as raw materials for industry. From corn and soybeans alone—two crops which have been carefully studied— more than five hundred different objects are manufactured. The principal industrial constituent of corn is starch, from which come many derivatives. The starch may be turned into dextrose or corn sugar, for many confectionery items, and for ice cream. The dextrose may be refined further and made into sorbitol, a product which consumers do not see, but which helps to keep bread moist.

Students of chemurgy emphasize the fact that, while botanists have identified more than a quarter of a million species of plants, not more than fifteen hundred, wild or cultivated, are utilized by man, and hardly more than three hundred are cultivated. Many of the others might well prove helpful, when scientists analyze them.

Not many years ago, for example, a new drug, reserpine, came into use as a tranquilizer. Derived from a species of snake-root, native to India, reserpine and drugs evolved from it have enabled tens of thousands of mentally-ill patients to resume normal lives.

Cortisone, which comes from plants like the wild yam, originally discovered in Mexico, is used to treat arthritis and other illnesses. New crops, such as safflower, yielding a valuable oil, and guar, grown for its industrially useful gum, are now planted on tens of thousands of acres, as are tung trees and castor beans, also producers of important oils. Papermakers are experimenting with bamboo as a possible source of cellulose.

When a new crop is seen to possess special values, the plant breeders go to work to increase these values. The soybean, for instance, has been bred into strains which are high in oil content, and into other strains which are high in protein.

In recent years, a farmer in Illinois has been experimenting with the starch in corn. The dominant starch molecule is globe-shaped, but other molecules are long and slender. This young man, Robert P. Bear, learned that if enough long slender molecules could be grown in the grain, a profitable new kind of starch could be produced. So far, he has succeeded in growing corn with more than sixty per cent of the long molecules. From it, transparent film has been made which, when used to wrap foods, can be eaten along with the contents.

Science has helped farmers to produce more meat at less cost. Vitamins, antibiotics, hormones, and enzymes added to feed in minute quantities bring amazing results. Many years ago, a broiler chicken needed five pounds of feed to add one pound of meat; now the chicken gains a pound on less than half that much feed. A tiny bit of a hormone with a six-syllable name—diethylstilbestrol—mixed in the feed, will put an extra ten to twenty per cent of fat on beef cattle.

Science has done much more to increase production than to discover new markets, but it is working on both fronts. Four large United States Department of Agriculture laboratories concentrate all their efforts on developing new food and industrial markets. And scores of private industries maintain research staffs, working in the same directions. As much as science has already accomplished in agriculture, new frontiers keep opening up, and many more are just beyond the horizon.

Under the American incentive system, thousands of men work to devise new mechanical and chemical aids that farmers will adopt, if the new things will make their work cheaper, easier, or more productive. Hundreds of processors, transporters, and distributors work to prepare and deliver the farmers' products in the form and condition the consumers will consider most attractive.

The consumer has the right to choose: the freedom to decide whose product will reach the family table. Built upon this structure, American agriculture has surpassed that of all the world; and free men, building in turn on the productivity of agriculture, have created an industrial and commercial economy that has no rival. All the American people are beneficiaries. The consumer who goes to the supermarket today finds that, although the dollar values have changed, he can buy much better food than forty years ago, and with the wages from practically the same number of hours of work. Moreover, fewer work hours are needed to buy a week's food supply here than in any country in the world.

The problems of present-day agriculture, have been well publicized. A surplus of wheat or corn, however, is a small problem indeed, when compared to the problems of hunger and malnutrition which even now, in the second half of the twentieth century, beset more than half of the world's people.

This great nation can face the future confident that food in abundance and variety will be ready for its increasing millions. Agriculture has grown from meager beginnings into a vast and productive industry with two hundred billion dollars worth of assets. Whenever the country needs more food, our farmers, if permitted the liberty to find their own ways, are prepared to increase even further their power to produce. Unless, by some tragic neglect or defeat, the liberties of Americans are lost, the United States will long be a land of plenty.

Index

133

About the Author

WHEELER MCMILLEN'S interest in agriculture is a life-long one. He was born on a farm in Ohio and went to a rural district school. After attending Ohio Northern University, he became a reporter, and then bought his own newspaper, a county-seat weekly. He ran the family farm for several years before he moved to New York as editor of *Country Home.* Later he joined *The Farm Journal* in Philadelphia as editor in chief.

Mr. McMillen is a past president of the Philadelphia Society for Promoting Agriculture and of the American Association of Agricultural Editors. He was executive director of President Eisenhower's Commission on Increased Industrial Use of Agricultural Products, a director of the Audubon Society, and a trustee of the Farm Foundation and of Rutgers University. He is now a vice-president of the National Council of the Boy Scouts of America and has received many awards from youth and patriotic organizations.